animal
behavior

Animal Behavior,
Paul A. Johnsgard
University of Nebraska

Understanding Evolution,
E. Peter Volpe
Tulane University

Animal Variety
Lawrence S. Dillon
A & M College of Texas

Principles of Development,
Norman S. Kerr
University of Minnesota

Animal Physiology
James Larimer
University of Texas

Plant Physiology
John B. Hanson
University of Illinois

Plant Diversity
Robert M. Harris
University of Arizona

**Animal Control
Mechanisms**
Benjamin W. McCashland
University of Nebraska

Cell Physiology
John G. Moner
University of Massachusetts

**Development of Biological
Ideas**
E. T. Pengelley
University of California

Principles of Genetics
Philip J. Snider
University of Houston

**Chemical Basis of
Cell Structure**
John H. D. Bryan
Iowa State University

Principles of Ecology
Eliot C. Williams, Jr.
Wabash College

Biology today is in the midst of profound and exciting revelations. This has resulted in a spectacular surge of biological knowledge and the consequent need for new approaches to the teaching of biology. The **Concepts of Biology Series,** designed for the introductory course, transmits the excitement of biology to the college student seeking a liberal education. The underlying theme of each book in the series is to foster an awareness of biology as an imaginative, evolving science. While the individual titles are self-contained, collectively they comprise a modern synthesis of major biological principles.

animal
behavior

PAUL A. JOHNSGARD
Associate Professor of Zoology
University of Nebraska

WM. C. BROWN COMPANY PUBLISHERS
Dubuque, Iowa

Manufactured by
WM. C. BROWN CO. INC., Dubuque, Iowa
Printed in U. S. A.

Introduction

Although the study of animal behavior is sometimes described as the newest branch of the zoological sciences, it is in a broader sense perhaps the oldest. There can be little doubt that early man's survival depended upon an intimate knowledge of animals and their behavior; doubtless the teaching of successful methods of stalking game was one of the pre-eminent concerns of early attempts at human communication. With the gradual development of agriculture man's dependence on wild animals declined, and a secondary interest in animals developed only with the general emergence of science. Such early writers as Aristotle and others included behavioral observations in their accounts of natural history, but it wasn't until the late 1800s that a true behavioral science began to emerge. From these beginnings not one but three distinct branches of the study of animal behavior differentiated independently, with little or no overlapping of concepts or methods. These three approaches, those of psychology, physiology, and ethology, have recently begun to show signs of fusion, with a consequent profitable sharing of techniques and concepts.

Recently, Kenneth Roeder, a distinguished neurophysiologist, has somewhat facetiously provided a ready means of distinguishing these three approaches. He has pointed out that the ethologist attempts to leave the animal as unrestricted as possible to study its "normal" behavior, and therefore tolerates any necessary discomforts while enclosing himself in a blind. The psychologist, in attempting to reduce the external variables, places the blind around the animal, thereby making it uncomfortable. The physiologist, in turn, probes directly into the nervous and motor systems of an animal in an attempt to learn what makes it behave.

The ethological approach, sometimes called the "naturalistic" or "comparative" study of animal behavior, will provide the mainstream of the present work, although it is hoped that physiological and psychological concepts will not be unduly neglected. Throughout the book, the concept of evolution will be a dominating issue, for the behavior patterns of present-day animals are as much a product of natural selection as is their anatomy.

During the writing of this book I received helpful advice and assistance from several people, including my colleagues in the Department of Zoology and Physiology of the University of Nebraska. Additionally, the entire manuscript was constructively reviewed by Dr. E. Kormandy, of Oberlin College. The five pages of line drawings were very kindly done for me by Mr. C. G. Pritchard, who exceeded my fondest wishes as to their accuracy and artistic qualities. The task of typing the manuscript was efficiently assumed by Mrs. Joan Wallick, who in the process happily rescued numerous dangling participles and reunited an even greater number of split infinitives. To my wife and children, for enduring the short tempers and redirected aggression brought on by preparing this book, and sometimes unknowingly providing inspiration for its contents, I simultaneously offer my apologies and thanks.

Contents

CHAPTER 1

Concepts and methods of behavior study

The writings of Aristotle are commonly used as a landmark indicating a formalization of the study of animals in general, and the same may be said of animal behavior. In his works may be found attempts to classify behavior patterns, to suggest possible relations between these behavioral categories, and to compare behavior patterns between species. Aristotle's recognition of behavioral similarities between species and groups that paralleled their classification on morphological grounds presaged by more than two thousand years Charles Darwin's evolutionary approach to the study of animal behavior. In Darwin's classic *Expression of the Emotions of Man and Animals,* he suggested that gestures and expressions shared by different but related species may be the result of common ancestry, and that both structure and "habits" might gradually evolve.

In spite of Darwin's fine theoretical foundation, the evolutionary approach to behavior temporarily foundered while an independent psychological approach prospered. In 1894, for example, C. Lloyd Morgan published a book on comparative psychology, in which his well-known principle of parsimony was spelled out: an animal's behavior should be interpreted in terms of the simplest possible "psychical faculty." With such an approach, the common pitfalls of anthropomorphism, the assigning of human capabilities to nonhumans, and teleology, the assumption of a known final purpose or design in an animal's behavior, could be readily avoided. The study of simpler forms of behavior in lower invertebrates was advanced by Jacques Loeb, whose theory of tropisms concerned simple directed responses of animals to differential stimulation. Herbert Jennings investigated the role of taxes and trial-and-error learning in invertebrates, and John B. Watson began to interpret animal behavior in simple stimulus-response terms. The appearance, in the 1920s, of Ivan Pavlov's theory of conditional reflexes provided important steps toward the establishment of modern psychological theory. The publication of Charles Sherrington's *Integrative Action of the Nervous System* in 1906 represented a masterful consolidation of theory and data for the developing neurophysiological school, and his fertile ideas dominated physiological research for nearly half a century.

THE DEVELOPMENT OF ETHOLOGY

With the exceptions of a few American workers such as George and Elizabeth Peckham, who contributed important early observations on the instinctive behavior of wasps, and Charles Whitman, who recognized the presence of stereotyped and taxonomically correlated components of pigeon behavior, the study of instinctive behavior gradually took shape in Europe quite independent of psychological theory. A new generation of English zoologists, reared in Darwinian thinking, began to interpret the breeding behavior of birds and other animals in terms of natural selection. The observations of such naturalists as Julian Huxley on the sexual behavior of the great crested grebe (*Podiceps cristatus*) and of H. Eliot Howard on the adaptive significance of territorial behavior in birds provide two examples of the early application of Darwinism to animal behavior. In Germany, Oskar Heinroth also grasped the biological and taxonomic significance of species-typical behavior patterns, and utilized this source of evidence for his classic survey of the waterfowl family Anatidae. Heinroth's paper introduced the word *ethology* for the study of such instinctive and species-typical behavior patterns, giving formal recognition to this evolutionary approach to the study of behavior. Partly because of a later realization of the impossibility of discretely separating instinctive and learned behavior patterns, ethology has since come to have a somewhat broader meaning than the study of strictly instinctive behavior, but the ethological interpretation of behavior in terms of survival value, natural selection, and evolutionary significance has never faltered.

Konrad Lorenz, a protégé of Heinroth, elaborated the ideas of this approach into its first formal theoretical framework. Lorenz avoided the anthropomorphic and teleological interpretations that still prevailed in describing animal responses, rejected a simple stimulus-response interpretation, and suggested that internal drives affect the activation of fixed patterns of automation. Lorenz believed that such hard "cores" of instinctive behavior, or *fixed action patterns* (FAP's), are inherited and accurately reflect the genome of any species in which they appear. The buildup of the drive that regulates the release of these FAP's results, according to Lorenz, from the increase of a reaction-specific energy, or *specific action potential* (SAP). In spite of this buildup of SAP, an animal theoretically will not normally perform the FAP except in the presence of a particular stimulus, the *sign stimulus*. Many species have evolved special devices, called *releasers,* which have as their primary or exclusive function the transmission of sign stimuli to others of their species. Such a releaser facilitates the expression of the FAP by triggering an *innate releasing mechanism* (IRM) in the central nervous system.

Lorenz's elaborate and mechanistic model clearly had many weaknesses, but it had one important advantage in that it avoided the interpreting the animal's behavior as a result of purposeful intentions. Instead, the seemingly directed activities were believed to result from inborn potential patterns of behavior which might be expressed and sequentially combined to result in a final biologically desirable goal, or *consummatory act.* In this way the early stages of such a behavioral series, which are often variable and may not be immediately rewarding (*"appetitive behavior"*), might be accounted for without ascribing purposeful intentions to the animal if they are viewed as part of a larger pattern of behavior having survival value to the species.

Since the work of physiologists such as Sherrington clearly indicated an organization of the nervous system closer in function to an electrical than to a hydraulic system, Lorenz's theory held little fascination for this group of workers. In an attempt to remove some of these objections Niko Tinbergen, an associate of Lorenz, introduced the idea of a hierarchical organization of behavior, and the visualization of the reaction-specific energy in terms of motivational impulses originating from various centers in the central nervous system. From these broad motivational centers a descending hierarchy of branching and more specific levels was hypothesized, finally terminating in specific fixed action patterns. The IRM's thus became regulators for the pathways determining the flow of impulses, and a system not unlike a radiating nervous network with regulating synapses emerged. By this concept an animal proceeds from a very generalized appetitive behavior through more predictable and specialized responses until a final consummatory act is achieved in the presence of the appropriate sequence of releasers. Further, the early and more variable stages of these sequences were regarded as those most likely to be affected by experience, whereas the final act was considered to be largely or entirely instinctive.

Tinbergen's visualization of the IRM's as "blocks" preventing continuous discharge of a spontaneously active center of nervous activity avoided the hydraulic pressure image of the SAP, but a strictly hierarchical organization makes it difficult to account for the possibility of widely different appetitive behavior patterns leading to the same consummatory act, or of a complex series of fixed action patterns occurring in rapid sequence without intervening appetitive behaviors. Also, some terminal responses are not, strictly speaking, consummatory acts, but rather tend to maintain a certain stimulus situation, with this simulus serving to inhibit further activity until it is removed or modified.

Both Lorenz and Tinbergen emphasized the adaptive significance of behavior, and argued that as an adaptive mechanism behavior should be studied under natural conditions where its adaptiveness is most apparent rather than under the artificial conditions imposed in the laboratory. Both also regarded instinctive behavior as something recognizably distinct from taxes, reflexes, and other simpler stereotyped responses.

The ethologists' insistence that instinctive behavior comprises a discrete category of responses resulted in criticisms from other workers, and the question of defining and identifying instinctive or "innate" behavior soon became a heated issue. Literally, instinct means "driven from within," and Darwin used the term to denote an innate urge for activity which results in a biologically desirable but essentially unknowable end. The ethologists have generally assumed that genetically fixed behavior coordinations or elaborate fixed action patterns stimulated by specific "releasers" are the hallmarks of instinctive behavior. According to their criteria, a response is considered instinctive if it is (1) constant in form, (2) characteristic of the species within the limits of expected individual variation, (3) capable of elicitation from animals raised in isolation, and (4) able to develop in animals prevented from practicing it. Frequently, however, the fulfillment of these last two criteria has been neglected.

The "innateness" of instinct, although central to the concept, can imply several different things. In common with reflexes, instinctive behavior is said to be innate in the sense that it is genetically fixed, or relatively free of learning influences. These "internally coordinated" responses are thus species-typical. The same may be said of reflexes, but, unlike reflexes, instinct is often said to have internal motivation or to possess an internal drive. When this drive implies something more deterministic than simple spontaneous nervous activity, such as specific and unitary "sex drives" and "hunger drives," teleological or vitalistic interpretations tend to replace objective descriptions. Substituting "SAP" or "tendency" for drive has been condemned as only exchanging the objectionable implications of drive for an equally unrealistic fluid-based interpretation of SAP or a judgment evaluation based on the observer's past experience. Besides this still unresolved question of internal motivation William Thorpe has listed three other diagnostic features of instinctive behavior. These include an inherited or genetically determined specificity, a complexity of responses usually greater than those of simple reflexes and often involving the coordination of several organ systems, and a sensitivity to and dependence upon complex environmental stimuli which the animal may appear to seek out purposefully.

In spite of recent criticisms of certain ethological concepts, these three criteria do seem to apply to a large group of behavioral patterns that can thus be distinguished from taxes, reflexes, and experience-dependent behavior. Furthermore, such patterns are found in a wide variety of animal species and groups that represent a considerable proportion of the animal kingdom. The evolution-oriented zoologist is therefore inclined to slight the fact that an adequate neurophysiological explanation of "instinctive" behavior is yet to be developed when functional explanations in terms of evolutionary adaptation can be applied. It need only be remembered that evolution itself was a useful concept long before Darwin provided the necessary theoretical mechanism of natural selection by which the evolutionary process could be satisfactorily explained.

METHODS OF BEHAVIORAL STUDIES

A frequent ethological approach to the study of behavior is to investigate thoroughly the total response repertoire of a single species. Such studies encompass all aspects of behavior including locomotor responses associated with foraging as well as bodily "comfort movements" such as preening, grooming, and bathing. Among invertebrate groups (Chapter 3) many innate responses associated with foraging and reproduction can be observed, and some vertebrate groups offer special opportunities for investigating learning abilities (Chapter 4). The locomotor abilities of animals, together with their investigational tendencies or ecological responses, may result in aggregations of individuals, raising the possibility of social interactions (Chapter 6). Social responses associated with attack and escape, or threat and submission, may provide a means of determining dominance relationships. Reproductive behavior patterns may be simple and concerned only with fertilization, or may be highly elaborate and subject to quantitative analysis. Various cooperative social responses may also be studied, especially in species exhibiting pair bonds or parental behavior. By studying the ontogeny of behavior (Chapter 5) in individuals under controlled conditions it is often possible to separate inherited and learned responses by experimentally regulating opportunities for the latter. This procedure is especially useful in the study of animal communication (Chapter 7), and by similar experiments information on the inheritance of behavior patterns may be obtained (Chapter 8). One may also attempt to determine the behavioral niche adaptations of a species in relation to its physical and biological environment (Chapter 9).

Alternatively, a comparative ethologist might study the corresponding behavior patterns in two or more related species in an attempt to obtain information of taxonomic application (Chapter 10), to reconstruct behavioral phylogenies, or to study the functions and evolution of species-typical "displays" within a group (Chapter 11). The process of *ritualization*, by which behavioral variations thus come to acquire "signal value" in communication, is believed to occur in the same manner as the evolution of structural variations between species. Frequently ritualization affects both the behavior and the morphology of a species as species-specific signals are evolved, and such display variations among related species may be significant factors in preventing interbreeding (Chapter 12).

Altering the conditions likely to affect a species' behavior has been a favorite technique of experimental ethologists. These conditions may be altered internally, through hormone injection, brain stimulation and the like, or externally, by modifying the normal releasing stimuli. Thus, it is possible to increase, decrease, or break down stimuli components, or to introduce choice situations between two slightly differing stimuli. In this manner it is sometimes feasible to define the exact "releasing" components of a stimulus, or to elicit strong responses from artificial "supernormal" stimuli. Through repeated stimulation the gradual waning of a motor response can also be studied.

Experimentation opportunities vary greatly among different species, but Niko Tinbergen and his students have shown that a remarkable number of simple experiments can be performed on wild animals through the clever use of models or by simple modifications of the environment. However, the number of uncontrolled variables in natural situations greatly increase the difficulties of obtaining significant differences resulting from the controlled variable. The semiconfined conditions of zoos, aquaria, or other collections of captive animals provide a compromise between the "typical" situation of wild animals and the highly artificial conditions which might prevail in a laboratory cage or testing apparatus. Here, controls over animal numbers, composition, social contacts, and opportunities for learning can be obtained, and certain kinds of experiments can be performed which would be impossible with unrestricted animals.

A variation of this last approach is to become a member of the animal's social group, either in the wild or in captivity. This technique is often highly difficult to attain but might provide an insight into the species' behavior that would otherwise be impossible to obtain. The most remarkable recent examples of this method are perhaps George Schaller's observations on wild mountain gorillas, and those of Jane Goodall on wild chimpanzees (Chapter 13).

One of the attractions of most early ethological studies was their simplicity of execution; no equipment separated the researcher from his subject, and the notebook and pencil were the primary tools, coupled with great patience and keen attention. For some species, binoculars or telescopes and blinds were needed as well. Recently it has sometimes proven useful to supplement these simple tools with motion picture cameras, portable dictaphones or tape recorders for recording observations or animals sounds, or using other devices for measuring animal activities. For example, nest activity recorders might measure incubation behavior, and cameras or counters might be automatically tripped when a particular activity occurs. Radar has been used to track bird flocks, and individuals have sometimes been tagged for visual recognition or for electronic tracking by telemetry. The human senses may be extended by such devices as infrared "snooperscopes" for night-time observations, and sound recorders sensitive to audible and supersonic frequencies are available. Such tape-recorded sounds may be later analyzed by audiospectrographic devices.

Even without all these elaborate labor-saving devices a great deal can still be learned by anyone with interest and initiative. Probably no species has been so thoroughly studied that it does not deserve further study, not even the most common domesticated animals. Whatever species is studied, accuracy of description can be assured only by repeated observations, not only of the behavior as observed in a given individual but also between individuals and in different situations. Quantitative note-taking, using symbols or prepared data sheets, will allow for later analysis of the data in ways unforeseen at the time of the original observations. In this way differences in frequencies, sequences, individuals' responses, and other variations may come to light and suggest new ideas. The use of timing devices no more complicated than a wrist watch will often be of help and may allow for a temporal analysis of behavioral variations. Finally, prior experience with other related species often gives an observer a keener insight or sensitivity to what he observes in a given species, and may allow him to recognize facets of behavior that would otherwise go unnoticed. This is especially true of sexual and other social behavior patterns, which may be differentially developed in related species, and may be more readily interpreted in them than in the species under primary study.

SUGGESTED READING °

ALTMAN, J., *Organic Foundations of Animal Behavior*. New York: Holt, Rinehart and Winston, Inc., 1966, 530 pp.

BIRNEY, R. C., and TEEVAN, R. C. (eds.), *Instinct*. Princeton, N. J.: D. Van Nostrand Book Company, Inc., 1961, 181 pp.

HINDE, R. A., *Animal Behavior: A Synthesis of Ethology and Comparative Psychology*. New York: McGraw-Hill Book Company, 1966, 534 pp.

‡ JESSOP, N. M., "Animal Behavior." *BioScience* 17:125-132, 1967. (A bibliography of 400 major references on animal behavior.)

LORENZ, K., *King Solomon's Ring*. New York: Thomas Y. Crowell, 1952, 202 pp. (Also available in paperback, Apollo Editions, New York.)

MARLER, P. R., and HAMILTON, W. J., III, *Mechanisms of Animal Behavior*. New York: John Wiley & Sons, Inc., 1966, 771 pp.

RATNER, S. C., and DENNY, M. R. (eds.), *Comparative Psychology: Research in Animal Behavior*. Homewood, Ill.: The Dorsey Press, Inc., 1964, 773 pp.

TINBERGEN, N., *Animal Behavior*. ("Life Nature Library.") New York: Time, Inc., Book Division, 1965, 200 pp.

READINGS FROM SCIENTIFIC AMERICAN. *Psychobiology: The Biological Bases of Behavior*. San Francisco: W. H. Freeman & Company, 1966, 382 pp. (This collection of offprints from Scientific American includes most of those listed in the Suggested Reading sections of the remaining chapters in this book.)

°The references listed here include a variety of texts and collections of research reports that survey the entire field of animal behavior.

CHAPTER 2

Anatomical and physiological bases of behavior

Except for the unicellular organization of protozoans, in which sensory and motor capabilities are organized within the organelle system, the fundamental units of the nervous system are the individual nerve cells, or *neurons*. Both systems are dependent upon a basic property of living material, irritability. Thus, even an ameba, which has no specialized receptor or motor elements, can gradually respond to a favorable or unfavorable localized stimulus in an adaptive way. However, increased efficiency of response may be assured by an arrangement in which specialized cells or parts of cells are more irritable (or "excitable") to certain stimuli than others; these *receptors* thus increase the organism's selective sensitivity. Provision for transmitting this information to other parts of the body may be achieved by special cellular extensions along which the cell's excited state can be conducted and ultimately transformed into meaningful responses by the organism through its appropriate *effectors*. In multicellular systems it is necessary that the information carried by the conducting neurons be able to bridge the gaps between cells; such neural connections are called *synapses*. The variably complex interplay of the different characteristics of receptors, neurons, synapses, and effectors is responsible for the integrated activity of the nervous system that results in the organized motor responses we recognize as behavior.

NEURONS

The basic unit of the multicellular nervous system is the neuron, which may vary in length, number of processes, and other characteristics, but still maintains a certain constancy of form and structure. Unlike other types of cells, it is characterized by extremely long, often branching, outgrowths from its *cell body*. The cell body includes the nucleus and a surrounding cytoplasm that often appears granular. These granules are made up of clumped ribosomes, rich in ribonucleic acid (RNA). From the cell body branched extensions, the *dendrites*, extend varying distances. A single long extension, the *axon*, is typically present. Unlike the dendrites, it is usually little branched except at the tip, where it branches repeatedly and comes into close synaptic contact with an effector or with the dendrites, cell body, or axon of another neuron. Terminal enlargements of these branches, the *boutons*, are typical of synaptic regions.

Although the axon, like the dendrites, may be a naked fiber, in vertebrates it is usually covered by an insulating sheath. This covering usually includes a fatty *myelin* layer within a cellular *neurilemma*, or sheath of Schwann. Peripheral myelinated nerves have *nodes of Ranvier* at regular intervals along the axon, where the insulating myelin layer is absent from the sheath of Schwann.

The classic idea of a neuron was one in which the dendrites were regarded as rather passive collectors of stimuli, passing these toward the cell body, then causing a rapid impulse to pass outward along the axon, eventually synapsing with another neuron or an effector tissue. This rather stringent view places the burden of integration on the synapse, since the only opportunity for variable neuron activity would lie in the frequency of the axon's impulse, or *action potential*. It is now believed that the dendrites may play an important role in integration as well. Unlike the all-or-none activity of the axon, the dendrites transmit impulses with graded and diminishing degrees and may introduce significant delays into the system. Through their complex branching, dendrites may receive information from numerous sources, perhaps thus allowing for synchronization of the activities of numerous neurons.

As a result of complex relative ion concentration changes inside and outside of the neuron membrane, dendrite stimulation may elicit an action potential in the axon, which typically travels rapidly and without diminution to the end of the neuron. The rate of impulse movement depends largely on the diameter of the neuron; thus for a given fiber the magnitude of the action potential and its rate of impulse transmission are constant regardless of the kind of stimulus that might have initiated the action potential. Myelinated fibers conduct action potentials much more rapidly than nonmyelinated ones; this is believed to be a result of discontinuous, or "saltatory," conduction between nodes of Ranvier rather than a continuous impulse as in nonmyelinated fibers.

Differences may occur in the frequency with which action potentials are generated, but after each there is a temporary refractory period, during which a neuron exhibits reduced capabilities for stimulation. So long as the stimulus producing the action potential remains, most neurons will tend to send additional impulses along the fiber. Information may thus be transmitted by variations in the number of action potentials and their temporal patterning. In some cases the frequency of action potentials increases with stimulation until a maximum rate is achieved. In others, however, the frequency is constant once a neuron is activated. Other situations include those where fixed-frequency bursts of impulses are generated or, as in the nerves associated with tactile responses in a cat's foot pad, there may be only a single action potential generated for touches of differing durations and intensities.

SYNAPSES

The point at which neurons come together and allow for an interneuron transfer of information is called a synapse. Synapses also connect neurons and effector organs, such as muscles, as for example at neuromuscular junctions. In both types, the axon of the presynaptic neuron subdivides into many small terminal branches, with boutons at their tips. Between these boutons and the postsynaptic membrane is an intervening space, or synaptic cleft. The boutons are known to contain many mitochondria as well as numerous submicroscopic vacuole-like structures, or synaptic vesicles.

Several features of the synapse set it apart from the action potential and suggest a basically different functional operation. These include (1) a delay in transmission, (2) an afterdischarge effect following cessation of stimulation, (3) a summation effect by which repeated stimulation may facilitate transmission when a single stimulus may have no effect, (4) a unidirectional transmission, and (5) a fatigability and susceptability to various drugs. Since an electrical hypothesis is inadequate to account for all these features, a chemical explanation has been advanced. By this hypothesis a transmitter substance is released by the boutons, diffuses across the synaptic cleft, and produces changes in the adjoining neuron that may cause a new action potential to be generated. Such a substance would have to be synthesized, stored, activated, and released by the presynaptic neuron, be able to react rapidly with the

11

postsynaptic neuron, and finally be broken down in a relatively short time. It is now known that acetylcholine is one of the most important of these chemical transmitters, and that the specific enzyme which breaks it down is cholinesterase. It is also known that certain transmitter substances may be inhibitory in function and thus prevent the generation of an action potential in the affected neuron; such interactions must clearly be important in coordinating the activities of antagonistic muscles.

Thus, the importance of synapses as regulators and integrators of nervous activity may be appreciated. Furthermore, if synaptic transmission efficiency is affected by frequency of use, as for example by becoming permanently more efficient through repeated use, a basis for behavioral changes through experience, or learning, can be visualized. There is some evidence that this is the case, as well as the reverse possibility, a loss of efficiency through extended disuse of synaptic pathways.

RECEPTORS

Sensory messages are initiated by specialized neurons or parts of neurons, called receptors, that are differentially sensitive to various forms of energy. In pain fibers of vertebrates, for example, free nerve endings near the skin provide for a simple kind of receptor in which mechanical pressures initiate impulses that are sensed as pain. Depending on the different kinds and specializations of these receptors, different numbers and kinds of senses can be recognized. Additionally, simple sensations can be integrated into more complex perceptions which may involve combinations of sight, sound, odor, and taste.

Regardless of whether the receptor is simple or complex, its operation depends on the transformation of some form of energy into action potentials. In this way receptors can be classified according to the kind of energy to which they are most sensitive: mechanoreceptors to pressure, photoreceptors to light, chemoreceptors to fluid- or air-borne substances, and thermoreceptors to heat or cold. Specific types of mechanoreceptors include stretch receptors, gravity receptors, and pressor receptors. Some animals exhibit highly specialized receptors operating beyond man's sensory limits, as for example the supersonic receptors of various bats and moths, the electroreceptors of certain fish, and the infrared receptors of pit vipers and the heat-loving *Melanophila* beetle.

Whatever the type of receptor, its stimulation results in a change in the cell's ionic concentrations that produces a receptor potential. Where the receptor is a part of the sensory neuron this receptor potential might directly initiate an action potential in that neuron. However, where the receptor comprises a separate cell it must stimulate an adjacent sensory neuron to produce an action potential. With continuous or repeated stimulation additional action potentials may be generated, but receptors typically diminish in their action potential output under constant stimulation, resulting in *receptor adaptation*. This rate of adaptation varies greatly in different types of receptors, with some exhibiting little or no adaptation (tonic receptors), whereas others may adapt completely (phasic receptors). Tonic receptor systems have a special importance in that they can accurately quantify information about the animal's environment. The phasic system, as illustrated by the tactile mechanoreceptors of a cat's foot pad, presumably provides much less qualitative or quantitative information about the condition of the substrate, but the information is transmitted immediately and the receptor is then "cleared" and ready to record the next event. The adaptive value of strictly tonic, phasic or intermediate kinds of receptor systems is readily apparent.

EFFECTORS

The means by which behavior occurs after motor neuron stimulation are through the activities of various effectors through which the motor neuron action potentials regulate an expenditure of energy. This may be mechanical energy, such as the contraction of muscle; glandular secretions of hormonal or enzymatic nature; generation of electricity by electric organs; production of light by luminous organs; or even changes in body coloration by chromatophore activity. As in typical synapses, the release of acetylcholine at the neuromuscular junctions of striated muscle has a chemical effect on the muscle fiber membrane that is transmitted into the myofibrils. This results in a rapid contraction along the length of the muscle fiber as an action potential is propagated in a manner similar to that occurring in neurons. Likewise, an all-or-none contraction response of the muscle occurs, which may be characterized as a rapid "twitch." The contraction of smooth muscle is under similar control, and the transmitter substance of one group of the controlling autonomic nerves is also acetylcholine. However, since the activated smooth muscle fibers are comprised of individual cells, the contraction is relatively slow and proceeds gradually. During stimulation of other autonomic motor nerves (the sympathetic group) a different transmitter substance, "sympathin," is present and has an effect opposite to that of acetylcholine. Thus, the release of sympathin (primarily noradrenalin) causes increased resistance to smooth-muscle contraction. Sympathic stimulation also causes the adrenal glands to release adrenalin and noradrenalin directly into the blood stream, where a diffuse effect results: a speeding up of the heartbeat, an increase in blood pressure, an increased blood circulation to the skeletal muscles, an increase in respiration, and an overall "fight or flight" reaction. Associated autonomic effects may also occur, such as hair erection, pupil dilation, sweating, and blushing, and may have no obvious adaptive value in such situations. These commonly recognized indications of this reaction may, however, have functional "signal" value in communicating the animal's internal state to others.

INTEGRATION OF NERVOUS ACTIVITY

Numerous opportunities for coordinating, regulating, and integrating nervous activity can be found at various functional levels, such as variations in receptor sensitivity, inhibition and excitation activities of the synapses, dendritic control of action potential propagation, and varied effects of different transmitter substances on effector organs. Thus, between the times of initial receptor stimulation and effector response, a number of controlling elements can be brought into play. Added to these complexities is the fact that various patterns of spontaneous activity of neurons can result in simple but regular cyclic patterns, or endogenous rhythms, of behavior independent of outside elicitations or control. Nonetheless, it is convenient to consider the *reflex* as one of the smallest readily measured segments of integrated behavior. Such a segment requires a minimum of a sensory and a motor neuron, one or more synapses, and a measurable effector response resulting from stimulation of a sensory neuron. Combinations of such simple reflexes may easily serve as the building blocks of more complex behavior patterns.

SUGGESTED READINGS

BUDDENBROCH, W. VON, *The Senses*. Ann Arbor: University of Michigan Press, 1958, 167 pp.

BULLOCK, T. H., "Physiological Bases of Behavior." In Moore, J. A. (ed.), *Ideas in Modern Biology*. Garden City, N. Y.: Natural History Press, 1965, pp. 449-482.

ECCLES, J., "The Synapse." *Scientific American*, January, 1965, pp. 56-66. (Available in offprint form from William H. Freeman & Company, Publishers, San Francisco.)

HARLOW, H. F., and WOOLSEY, C. N. (eds.), *Biological and Biochemical Bases of Behavior*. Madison: University of Wisconsin Press, 1958, 476 pp.

KATZ, B., "How Cells Communicate," *Scientific American*, September, 1961, pp. 209-220. (Available in offprint form.)

———, *Nerve, Muscle, and Synapse*. New York: McGraw-Hill Book Company, 1966, 193 pp.

KRNJEVIC, K., "Chemical Transmission in the Central Nervous System." *Endeavor* 25(94): 8-12, 1966.

OCHS, S., *Elements of Neurophysiology*. New York: John Wiley & Sons, Inc., 1965, 621 pp.

WILSON, V. J., "Inhibition in the Central Nervous System." *Scientific American*, May, 1966, pp. 102-110.

CHAPTER 3

Invertebrate organization and behavior

Although the neuron is the basic unit of the nervous system in multicellular animals, a relatively simpler situation exists in the protozoans. Some advanced groups of ciliates do exhibit an intracellular neuron-like, or *neuroidal*, organization analogous in function to neurons, but no such structural basis for behavioral responses can be detected in the less specialized protozoans. These nonetheless can often react to a wide variety of environmental stimuli, including heat, light, and mechanical, chemical, and electrical sources of energy. Undirected motor responses produced by different intensities of stimulation are called *kineses*, and may eventually result in an adaptive change in the animal's orientation with respect to that stimulus. Through changes in the speed of movement or frequency of movement the animal may achieve a position which elicits no further response to the stimulus.

In amebas, pseudopodia may be extended directly toward a stimulus through chemotactic attraction. Such directed positive or negative responses to a stimulus source, termed tropisms or *taxes*, result from oriented motor responses to differential stimulation. A bending or twisting (*klinotaxis*) of the body is typical if only a single sensory receptor is present, since it must measure stimulation intensity on each side alternately. With paired receptors present it may be possible to orient relative to a stimulus by achieving balanced stimulation in the two receptors (*tropotaxis*) or by direct orientation using one or both receptors (*telotaxis*).

Protozoans may also exhibit relatively specialized receptors, such as the light-sensitive stigma of plantlike flagellates such as *Euglena*.

The ciliate *Euplotes* has several coordinating and presumably conducting fibers that regulate ciliary movement, and a variety of other effectors such as flagella and contractile fibrils, or myonemes, occur in some advanced ciliates. Among such ciliates some surprisingly complex behavior patterns can be seen. Many ciliates are continually active, feeding constantly through their ciliary action. In *Vorticella* materials are selectively accepted or rejected as they are swept into the buccal cavity through the regulation of the direction of ciliary movements. If repeatedly exposed to unsuitable materials, a *Vorticella* may contract, bend over, or swim away to a new location. Another ciliate, *Didinium*, swims randomly about with its armored mouth directed forward, penetrating any object it might meet. Edible objects are then swallowed, and inedible ones are rejected. Occasionally one *Didinium* will attach to another, at times forming chains of several, but they never manage to swallow their congeners. Even solid objects such as glass will be repeatedly attacked in futile attempts to penetrate them. So far no convincing experiments proving a long-term adaptive modification of behavior as a result of past experience have been achieved with protozoans.

COELENTERATES

The first structural advance toward an integrated multicellular nervous system may be seen in the *nerve net* of the coelenterates, in which individual neurons and synapses can be recognized, as well as photoreceptors, chemoreceptors, gravity receptors, and glandular and muscular effectors. The nervous system of coelenterates is basically a dual system, with both general and local control. Throughout the animal there is a diffuse network of multipolar neurons which conduct impulses in all directions, producing a rather low and graded response that varies with distance and degree of stimulation. But the free-swimming medusae forms also have a discrete linear system of neurons organized into a *nerve ring* near the margin of the bell, which is closely associated with specialized receptors for gravity and light. This nerve ring is made up of bipolar neurons which conduct impulses to the muscles relatively rapidly, with no loss of strength as they are transmitted. In this case, there is little dependence upon the gradual diffuse spread of a motor response through the nerve network as a result of repeated stimulation. Rather, the controlling centers are in the sensory areas of the margin which serve to automatically regulate and synchronize the muscular contractions needed to maintain effective swimming. Removing all these marginal bodies will prevent muscle contraction in the scyphozoan *Aurelia*, but allowing a single body to remain is sufficient for maintaining the regulative *pacemaker* effect. The nerve ring itself exhibits no centralized dominance in pacemaker rhythm; the most active body evidently establishes the overall contraction pattern. Thus, cutting the ring will usually have little effect on contraction rhythm, and isolated margins containing the nerve ring will continue to contract regularly.

The hydrozoan medusa *Gonionemus* exhibits some interesting behavioral adaptations. In the presence of food it makes random searching movements, indicating a chemical sensitivity to water-borne stimuli, whereas other medusae often require actual contact with the food. *Gonionemus* also "fishes" by swimming to the surface, turning upside down, and slowly floating downward with its tentacles widely spread. In some scyphozoan medusae a "righting reflex" dependent upon marginal statocysts is definitely present, causing the raised side of a tilted medusa to contract strongly and remain contracted until the pulsations of the lowered side return it to a horizontal position.

Intact or isolated arms of such scyphozoans as *Aurelia* and *Cyanea* are sensitive to a wide range of proteins and protein components in the elicitation of feeding responses. However, certain species of fish regularly retreat under medusae of various kinds without being stung, and several kinds of crustaceans have been found living in the arm frills of scyphozoan medusae.

Among the relatively muscular anemones some species move by a gliding muscular movement of the pedal disk while others may use their tentacles for "walking" or may even swim by tentacular movement. Anemone tentacles are usually highly sensitive to chemostimulation and may exercise some discrimination in their foraging responses. Individual tentacles may become "satiated" with food, probably through a gradual reduction in receptor sensitivity, or sensory adaptation, while other tentacles of the same animal may continue to feed actively on the same material.

A remarkable behavioral association exists between certain species of anemones and hermit crabs. An anemone is often attached to the adopted shell of a hermit crab, thereby gaining for the crab a degree of protection, while the anemone, in turn, obtains transportation and increased food availability, a mutually beneficial arrangement for both species. Some species of fish, being immune to the dangers of the anemone tentacles, may use these as safe retreats and possibly even lure other less adapted species to their death as they try to follow them. Some such anemone fish (*Amphiprion*) are brightly colored and regularly live in association with the anemone, another example of behavioral *mutualism*.

Of special interest are the changes in thresholds of sensitivity to food in anemones as a result of satiation produced by sensory adaptation or muscular fatigue. Although a hungry anemone will sometimes accept inedible objects such as sand, paper, and the like, it soon begins to reject these items, even though it may accept meat. Such a differential response to significant and insignificant stimulation is clearly adaptive. This apparent discrimination may be a result of the factors mentioned above, or possibly represents a very simple form of learning. In this case it appears that the physiological explanations are more likely, since, as the feeding response diminishes, the anemone first fails to react to weak stimuli, such as paper or paper soaked in meat juices, and only later does it fail to respond to meat itself.

In summary, the coelenterates exhibit well-defined taxes relative to light, gravity, and food, and simple behavior patterns that might be reasonably described as reflexes. Local responses are generally more conspicuous than centralized control, and there is no indication of centralized integration of nervous activity. Sensory adaptation and motor fatigue play important roles in modifying behavioral responses, and nearly all of any species' behavioral repertoire is concerned with foraging. The radial organization of the body and nervous system is an inherent limitation of coelenterates and one that can also be observed in the echinoderms, the only other major phylum organized with radial symmetry. The evolution of a bilaterally symmetrical body, with its resulting somatic division into anterior-posterior, dorsal-ventral, and right-left planes, opens the way to streamlining, the development of a head, and the ensuing clustering of sensory and integrative mechanisms in the head region (encephalization). The turbellarian flatworms can be used as an example of a group in which the advantages of bilateral symmetry and encephalization may be seen.

PLATYHELMINTHES

In the free-living flatworms, the turbellarians, it is possible to trace the development of a centralized nervous system. Although a diffuse nerve net of multipolar neurons is still found, there is also a congregation of more linear fibers arranged in several anterior-posterior nerve tracts. The cell bodies of these fibers tend to occur in groups (*ganglia*), and such ganglia may be found at regular intervals along the several anterior-posterior tracts, usually with lateral connections. Ganglia are especially well developed near the sensory structures of the head region. Probably the *cerebral ganglion,* or "brain," evolved in association with the hydrozoan-like statocyst of the head region, but gradually assumed more generalized functions and, indeed, the statocyst is lacking in advanced turbellarians.

Among some primitive (or retrogressive) turbellarians there is a general nerve net just below the epidermis and best developed near the head, but only a slight indication of longitudinal fiber development. In other turbellarians this nerve net is deeper, next to the inner surface of the subepidermal muscles. From three to six distinct longitudinal pairs of fiber tracts are typically present, but a ventral pair is usually most prominent. This condition may be a forerunner of the solid, paired ventral nerve cords typical of invertebrates in general. The cerebral ganglion lies at the anterior tip of these paired ventral cords. This ganglion consists of internally organized fiber tracts and peripheral cell bodies, usually in close proximity to sensory receptors. The ventral tract contains numerous unipolar motor cells which extend their long axon processes into the muscle fibers.

Sensory receptors in turbellarians may include gravity-sensitive statocysts, tactile cells (*tangoreceptors*) with hairlike surface projections, *chemoreceptors* occurring primarily in ciliated pits or grooves, *photoreceptors* associated with pigment cups (*ocelli*), and probable water-current receptors (*rheoreceptors*). As a result, it is not surprising that these animals exhibit a variety of taxes. These include *geotaxes* (negative or positive), *thigmotaxes* (positive to touch on ventral surface, negative dorsally), *chemotaxes* (positive to food in water, weak acids, and other weak chemicals), *phototaxes* (generally negative), *rheotaxes* (positive in stream-dwelling species), some degree of *thermotaxes* (a response threshold to differences of two to three degrees Centigrade), and *galvanotaxes* (attracted to the cathode, as are ciliate protozoans).

Nearly all turbellarians are hermaphroditic, with complex reproductive systems. Mutual *internal fertilization* by copulation or hypodermic injection of sperm is typical of turbellarians, and these represent the lowest animal group to exhibit this behavior. Copulation is preceded by head or body contacts, a primitive form of "courtship" that may serve to identify the species or stimulate the other individual. Sperm or sperm packets (*spermatophores*) may be discharged into special receiving structures or may be injected, by means of an armed penis, into the mesenchyme of the other individual. The evolutionary advantages of internal fertilization, in terms of gamete efficiency and opportunities for prevention of interspecific fertilization, cannot be overemphasized. Furthermore, internal fertilization is a necessary prerequisite for a land-dwelling existence, which is typical of some planarians.

In the turbellarians the first good examples of adaptive behavioral modifications resulting from experience, or *learning*, can be found. Besides the possibility of *habituation*, or gradually learning not to respond to an unimportant repeated stimulus, there may also be a positive *reinforcement* of a response to significant stimulation, resulting in lowered response thresholds. These reduced or increased tendencies to respond to a particular stimulus represent simple forms of *associative learning*, in which the animal comes to associate a particular stimulus with a significant or insignificant effect, and modifies its response accordingly. Thus, the slightly negatively phototactic turbellarian *Stenostomum* can be trained to turn back more regularly toward the dark at a light-dark boundary after it has been repeatedly exposed to an electric shock when it enters the lighted area. It is much more difficult to train the animal to perform the opposite response, which is contrary to its normal negative phototaxis. Very similar results have been obtained with fresh water planarians, using such contrasting stimuli as substrate surface, light intensity, and horizontal *vs.* vertical planes. Positive evidence indicating the effect of experience in partially inhibiting the general tendency of turbellarians to move when exposed to light has been obtained for a polyclad species, which was subjected to alternating periods of dark (thirty minutes) and light (five minutes). When the light was turned on and the animal began to move away, it was touched on the anterior margin. With experience, fewer touches were required to reduce the light-stimulated movement, although it was never completely inhibited. Destruction of the cerebral ganglion prevented such simple learning.

The experiments just mentioned are essentially examples of a general method of testing for simple associative learning, *classical conditioning*. In this technique, an attempt is made to train an animal to associate two essentially simultaneous but normally unrelated stimuli, having different associated responses. Thus, Pavlov trained a dog to salivate (conditioned reflex) at the sound of a bell (conditioned stimulus), when the latter was associated with food presentation (unconditioned stimulus),

21

for which salivation is a normal reaction (unconditioned reflex). When an animal regularly performs the conditioned reflex in the presence of the conditioned stimulus alone, it is said to be "conditioned." The rate of development and relative retention of this acquired response may be used as a measure of simple learning. For example, when a planarian is suddenly exposed to light it will tend to stretch, probably as a preliminary to moving out of the lighted area. Its unconditioned response to an electric shock is to contract or turn its head. After about 100 conditioning trials in which a sudden exposure to light is followed by a shock, the planarian will usually have acquired a conditioned reflex, that is, to contract or turn its head when exposed to light alone. With time, this response will be largely forgotten unless it is reinforced with the light-shock combination, although a subsequent conditioning will generally require a shorter training period. This experiment suggests that there is a certain retention, or *memory*, of the acquired response.

Since planarians exhibit a remarkable degree of regenerative ability, an opportunity is present to test for the anatomical localization of this "memory." Thus, conditioned animals have been cut in half and allowed to regenerate their missing heads or tails. Such animals tend to exhibit some memory of the conditioned response, whether they are derived from either the original head or the original tail end. However, if the cut halves are allowed to regenerate in a solution containing ribonuclease (an enzyme that selectively breaks down RNA), only the individuals that represent the original head ends were reported to retain a partial memory, as estimated by the reduced number of retraining trials needed to establish a fully conditioned response again. Even more remarkably, it has been reported that when conditioned planarians were cut up and fed to unconditioned animals, the latter exhibited a significantly reduced training time to achieve fully conditioned responses. If reliable, these experiments would have important implications as to the biochemical basis of learning, to be considered in the next chapter. But such experiments have been criticized on various grounds such as insufficient sample size and lack of adequate controls. An elaborated repetition of the last experiment, in which unconditioned planarians were allowed to cannibalize others that had previously been exposed to light, handling, or previous conditioning, showed that such individuals all conditioned more rapidly than did completely naive planarians, suggesting that other factors, possibly related to nutrition, might affect conditioning rate.

INSECT ORGANIZATION

As an example of the culmination of the trends that are discernible in the flatworms, the structural and behavioral characteristics of insects might be examined as being representative of the acme of invertebrate nervous organization. In the arthropods, the ventral longitudinal nerve cords, which are basically double but largely fused, are established as the primary conducting pathways, and thus a *central nervous system* is fully achieved. The cerebral ganglion, or *brain*, has gained an ascendency in size and control over the more posterior ganglia, which are developed, one ganglion per segment, in a magnitude corresponding to the particular motor importance of that segment. Thus, the three large separate or fused thoracic ganglia control the important walking legs and wings, and the smaller abdominal ganglia exercise local control in that region. The *peripheral nervous system* includes the dorsal sympathetic system innervating the gut and the ventral sympathetic system leading to the spiracles.

The organization of the body into its variably differentiated *heteronomic segmentation* allows for structural specialization of different body parts, with a consequent increase in efficiency. In addition, the chitinous exoskeleton is admirably suited to the development of specialized effector structures for grasping, pinching, cutting, boring, sound production, and other acts. Furthermore, the arthropods illustrate an important integrative and regulative behavioral control, the secretion of *hormones* by neurons, producing a functional *neuroendocrine* system. A major neurosecretory center in insects is the median *pars intercerebralis* of the brain. These cells secrete a hormone, temporarily stored in the lateral *corpora cardiaca*, which upon release into the hemolymph stimulates a strictly endocrine gland in the thorax, the *prothoracic gland*. This, in turn, secretes a hormone that stimulates molting. The *corpora allata* represent the last of the known major endocrine structures of insects, secreting a hormone (juvenile hormone) that prevents metamorphosis during molting. Additional scattered or clustered neurosecretory cells occur in the brain or ventral ganglia of insects, and in a few cases are known to be physiologically active.

In insects, hormones are known to regulate several general types of behavior. For example, hormones may affect *cryptic behavior*, or the ability to change color to match the background. This ability is shared by such insects as some grasshoppers, stick insects, caterpillars, and lepidopteran pupae. Hormones may also regulate *rhythmic* behavior, or the occurrence of *endogenous rhythms* of activity, often in cycles of about twenty-four hours (circadian rhythms). Furthermore, hormones may influence behavior patterns associated with *sexual activity, molting,* and *social behavior* patterns in the truly social insects.

Some hormones are able to exert a physiological effect in individuals other than those which produced them. Such *ectohormones,* or *pheromones,* often have a remarkable effect on the behavior of other individuals, through their transmission by direct ingestion of these secretions (*trophallaxis*) or their diffusion through the air. These effects may be immediate and long-lasting, often apparently directly affecting the central nervous system and "releasing" a specific behavior pattern in the recipient. Thus, they may stimulate searching behavior in a male moth that has been exposed to the air-borne secretions of a virgin female of its species. Alternatively, the pheromone may have an indirect "primer" effect, stimulating a series of physiological processes that may ultimately affect behavior. Several different pheromones may be produced by the same species and have very different effects; in ants, for example, they may serve as alarm signals or as guidance signals to food or new nest sites.

One of the most remarkable features of insects is the variety and sensitivity of their sensory receptors, in particular their chemoreceptors, photoreceptors, and mechanoreceptors. The chemical senses of insects include both fluid-borne *taste* and air-borne *smell,* as well as a general chemical contact sense. These regulate a host of vital behavior patterns including foraging, habitat selection, sex attraction, host-parasite relations, and other activities.

The visual receptors include the compound eyes, typical of nearly all adult insects, as well as the simple ocelli found in larvae and adults of many insects. Like the "eyes" of planarians, the ocelli probably produce no real images, but have been believed to serve, perhaps, in regulating the sensitivity of the compound eyes, a view not presently in favor. The compound eye, with as many as 28,000 individual ommatidia, is an image-forming eye with marked efficiency in the detection of movement and, to a more limited degree, shape. Two aspects of special behavioral significance are the capacity for at least some insects to perceive both visible and ultraviolet light, as well as an ability to detect planes of polarized light. Thus, the great potential of the insect eye for evaluating differences in shape, color, brightness, object movement, and other visual parameters is paramount in regulating many of their behavioral capabilities. The occurrence of species-specific color patterns of butterflies, the various flashing characteristics of fireflies, and the colors and shapes of flowers normally pollinated by insects thereby take on special adaptive significance.

Mechanoreceptors in the insects are particularly well developed and varied in function, since the chitinous exoskeleton is favorably endowed with capacities for structural plasticity. The basic touch receptor is the sensory hair, which may occur singly or in clusters. Gravity and pressure senses are interrelated in insects, and rarely are true statocysts to be found in the group. However, "external statocysts," in the form of air bubbles trapped within sensitive hair structures, do occur in some aquatic insects. In the majority of insects it appears that proprioceptors located at the numerous joints provide for gravity perception under most conditions. While in flight, insects must utilize special sensory structures of certain areas to maintain their equilibrium, such as hair plates in the neck region of dragonflies and bees, or the gyroscope-like halteres of the Diptera. Orientation to moving currents of water (*rheotaxis*) or air (*anemotaxis*) may be achieved by the stimulation of hairs on the head or antennae. Hairlike tactile receptors responsible for interpreting contacts with solid surfaces are numerous and widespread, and often serve the additional function of chemoreception. Sensitivity to rapid oscillations of the substrate (*vibration sense*) or of a fluid or aerial environment (*hearing*) is also common. Capacities for hearing vary greatly in insects, but this ability is especially typical of such sound-producing groups as some of the Orthoptera (grasshoppers, katydids, and crickets) and Homoptera (cicadas). In these an elaborate system of *acoustical communication* has evolved, often with highly specialized sound receptors (*tympanal organs*) on the thorax, abdomen, or forelegs.

The types of effectors to be found in insects are just as numerous and complex as the receptors. Distinct from the separate smooth musculature of the digestive tract, the striated muscles concerned with bodily movement are numerous. Unlike the situation in the flatworms, the body muscles are organized into discrete bundles that may link adjacent parts of the exoskeleton and gain the mechanical advantages provided by levers formed from the exoskeleton.

The evolution of *wings* in insects has particular behavioral significance, and it has been suggested that they evolved from flaps on the thoracic notum that originally served as sexual display structures before being modified into flight structures.

The capacity for some insects, including several families of Coleoptera, the larvae of two families of Diptera, and a few additional species, to emit light represents a highly specialized type of effector worthy of special interest. Among the larval dipterans this light appears to function in attracting other insects, which are caught in sticky threads secreted by the carnivorous larvae. In the true fireflies (Lampyridae) the flashing serves largely as a mating device, and may be produced by the female or by both sexes. In the latter case there is usually a sexual dimorphism of flashing behavior, and opportunities for both species recognition and mutual sexual attraction through these specific visual signals are possible.

Another group of effectors of behavioral importance are the sound-producing, or *stridulation*, structures of insects. These specialized effectors mostly fall into two categories, those employing simple frictional mechanisms and those utilizing membrane vibration to achieve sound production. The frictional technique involves a *scraper and file* combination, in which a knoblike scraper is rubbed over a ridged or serrated file, producing a rasping sound capable of a wide frequency range and diverse modulation patterns in different species, although individual species exhibit little frequency variation. In the Orthoptera, such devices are usually located on the two elytra (as in crickets and katydids) or on the elytron and femur (as in short-horned grasshoppers). In other groups the abdomen, head, or thorax may also be involved, and clearly such diverse mechanisms have independently evolved on many occasions. The cicadas utilize a much more complex method of sound production, in which a *tymbal organ* is vibrated. This thin and convex membrane is alternately snapped inward by a special muscle and allowed to snap backward, producing a double sound.

Insect-produced sounds may have numerous functions. These include attraction of the opposite sex, aggressive responses, fostering of social groups, serving as alarm or warning sounds, and providing specific guidance signals, as is known to be the case in honeybees. Crickets typically produce as many as six different sounds during reproduction. Sounds may also be secondarily utilized by predators or parasites for locating their prey or host species. For example, the female wasp *Chlorion* is attracted to her cricket prey through its stridulation. Contrariwise, some moths are highly sensitive to the ultrasonic sounds produced by hunting bats, and thus are sometimes able to evade them.

INSECT BEHAVIOR

With this vast array of specialized receptors, effectors, and a complex central and peripheral nervous system, we might expect a behavioral capability in insects far exceeding that of the groups previously mentioned. Indeed, in their stereotypy and predictability of complex behavior the insects are perhaps unmatched.

A wide variety of taxes can be demonstrated in insects, one of the most remarkable being the time-compensated *light-compass reaction*, demanding not only a directed movement in relation to the sum or planes of polarized light, but also a compensation for the apparent change in the sun's position with time, which requires both an "internal clock" and an ability to estimate accurately the position of the sun. Such light-compass reactions have been demonstrated in bees, certain beetles and other insects. Light-compass reactions that are not time-compensated (*menotaxes*) are also known; interrupting such movements until the sun has moved some distance across the sky will result in displaced orientation in these insects. Menotaxes that are gravity-oriented are also known, and occur in bees, ants, and other insects. Honeybees are even able to transpose their sun-compass orientation into a gravity orientation. This ability is the basis of the famous waggle dance of the worker bee, in which the horizontal angle of the food relative to the sun is transposed into an equivalent angle away from the vertical plane.

In such ways, taxes and reflexes are incorporated into more complex "instinctive" behavior patterns, and no clear line can be drawn between these types of sterotyped behaviors. Some instincts appear to be chains of simple reflexes for which the brain is not really needed; thus, an isolated female silkworm abdomen is able to copulate and lay eggs. A headless male praying mantis automatically performs copulatory movements, which may be of adaptive value, since female mantids are known occasionally to consume the head of the male during copulation. Decapitated female *Drosophila* are actually able to walk, preen, and fly, and will be courted by males, suggesting that the brain may serve to initiate, regulate, or inhibit behaviors that are "fixed action patterns" of a lower neural level.

Instinctive behavior patterns of insects typically (1) require a releaser, (2) exhibit varied thresholds of performance including spontaneity and "exhaustibility," (3) are relatively species-specific and independent of learning, and (4) are adaptive. Like the fixed action patterns, releasers are also usually species-specific, although interspecific recognition and responses are not uncommon. Two German ethologists, H. Markl and Martin Lindauer, have recently stated that the original releaser concept was too restrictive, and suggest that *signaling devices* be used instead of releasers. This term would encompass both signaling structures (color, pattern, shape) and signaling behavior (movements, sounds, odors), include functions of either stimulating or inhibiting responses, and incorporate both interspecific and intraspecific interactions.

As an example of insect behavior interpreted in ethological terms, the hunting behavior of certain solitary wasps might be used. These "predatoid" wasps include the groups in which the female seeks out a relatively specific prey, paralyzes it, deposits an egg on or near it, and seals it up where it will remain available for the larva when it hatches. This apparent foresight of these wasps might, at first glance, appear to represent a high order of calculated behavior. However, a few examples will show how such complex patterns can be broken down into simpler and rigid fixed action patterns.

The female digger wasp *Ammophila pubescens* (or *"adriaansei"*) performs a series of responses that can be broken into three general categories, always performed in the same sequence. First, it digs a nest, hunts for a caterpillar, paralyzes it, drags it back to its nest, and deposits an egg on it. Next, it brings more caterpillars, and after each one it temporarily closes the nest when it leaves. Finally, after bringing the last caterpillar, it permanently closes the nest and abandons it. Remarkably, up to three nests in differing stages of completion are often tended simultaneously. However, each phase of a particular nesting sequence is rigidly adhered to, and appears to be dependent on specific stimuli.

This pattern is species-specific, and related species differ in details. For example, a morphologically identical species, *A. campestris*, oviposits the egg prior to provisioning, preys on sawflies, and also differs in certain other minor aspects of behavior. Some species of *Ammophila* provision the nest with a single large caterpillar, whereas others may use a dozen or more smaller ones. Furthermore, it has even been found that in certain species the female uses a small pebble, held in her mandibles, to tamp down the earth over the entrance to the nest before abandoning it for the last time.

Wasp species that prey on caterpillars typically sting them in nearly every body segment, thus rendering ineffective each of the somatic ganglia in turn. Finally the head region is bitten, preventing further use of the jaws, but not going so far as to kill the caterpillar, which must remain edible until the wasp larva is able to consume it. But in the spider-hunting species, or those that prey on adult insects, stinging is performed only in the region of the thoracic ganglia, which control the walking appendages. This apparent innate knowledge of the neuro-anatomy of the prey species has caused much wonder, but is, of course, readily explained through natural selection, resulting in a greater reproductive efficiency among those wasps that more effectively render their prey immobilized without killing it or being killed themselves. Such efficiency is especially vital for the spider hunters such as the tarantula hawk *Pepsis*, which faces an enemy several times larger than itself and one which is equipped with an effective defense in the form of its thick exoskeleton and venomous chelicerae. However, the wasp always manages to insert her sting into the only vulnerable point that will enable her to reach the vital thoracic ganglia, the soft membrane at the junction of the leg and thorax.

To prove the inflexibility of these fixed action patterns and the resulting inability of the insect to cope with external tampering, one may modify experimentally some link in the sequence and observe the results. For example, an *Ammophila* female tending several nests will inspect each of these in the morning and later bring in prey to these according to needs. However, if the food supply in the nest is altered after the inspection flight, the female will still leave the amount of food there when she returns that was indicated by the morning visit. Richard Hingston reported that if a cricket, the prey of *Sphex lobatus*, is presented to a female of this species while she is in the process of digging open a cricket's den, the wasp will become agitated but will not attack it. Evidently the stimulus for stinging lies in the expulsion of the cricket from its own den, and the chain of effective fixed action patterns is thus prevented by the absence of one link.

A similar case was described by the French naturalist J. Henri Fabri, who studied another species of *Sphex*. In this species the cricket, after being subdued, is dragged back to the wasp's burrow and pulled in. The incarceration is done in several stages. The female drops the paralyzed cricket near the entrance, runs inside the burrow, then emerges and pulls the cricket inside. While the female was inside the burrow, Fabri moved the immobilized cricket a few inches away from the entrance. The wasp emerged, searched for the cricket, pulled it back to the entrance, dropped it, and again disappeared into the burrow. Fabri repeated this trick forty times, and each time the wasp failed to complete the act of pulling the cricket all the way into the nest.

Not only are insects often incapable of "skipping" a link in a series of fixed action patterns, but also they are frequently incapable of repeating a link or performing it out of sequence. Thus, Richard Hingston found a nest of the digger wasp, *Psammophila tydei,* in which the victim, a caterpillar, had been placed, the egg laid on it, and the female was in the process of gathering small pebbles to cover the entrance. Hingston removed the single caterpillar and attached egg from the burrow, placing them at the burrow's entrance. When the wasp returned, it continued to fill the empty burrow, not only in view of the caterpillar and egg but even treading on them in the process. It finally filled the burrow and smoothed it over normally as if nothing at all were unusual about the situation. The inadequacy of these normally efficient fixed action patterns in an unpredictable environment becomes glaringly apparent under such conditions, and points out the important advantages of flexible behavior over stereotyped responses.

Sometimes the signaling devices of an insect species are utilized by another species for its own benefit. For example, the conspicuous patterning and generally similar coloration found in most wasps is regarded as a form of warning coloration, and after a single unpleasant experience with a wasp, potential predators are likely to leave creatures of such appearance alone. However, this "wasp-like" signal has been closely mimicked, in form, pattern and behavior, by a number of innocuous insects (Fig. 1). A Brazilian grasshopper, *Scaphura nigra,* runs with extended wings in the manner of a *Pepsis* wasp, and several kinds of insects bend the abdomen as if about to sting when captured. An Australian wasp, *Abispa ephippium,* is visually mimicked in color and pattern by a variety of insects representing such diverse orders as beetles, moths, and flies. Although such nonwasps lack the thin "waist" of the true wasps, some have even evolved a contrasting color pattern that suggests a narrow waist. Possibly the most remarkable example of "stolen" signaling devices is to be found in the orchids of the genus *Ophrys,* the flowers of which are scented, shaped, and colored in such a way as to attract male wasps of certain species, which, in attempting

Fig. 1. Signaling Devices and Signaling Behavior. Warning pattern of a wasp (A), compared with pseudo-warning pattern of a clear-wing moth (B) (after Portmann). Cryptic resting attitude (C) and pseudo-warning snake-like attitude (D) of sphinx moth larva (after Cott). Warning display of mantid (after Cott). Mimicry of female wasp (G) by *Ophrys* orchids (G & H), resulting in pollination of males (I) (after Kullenberg).

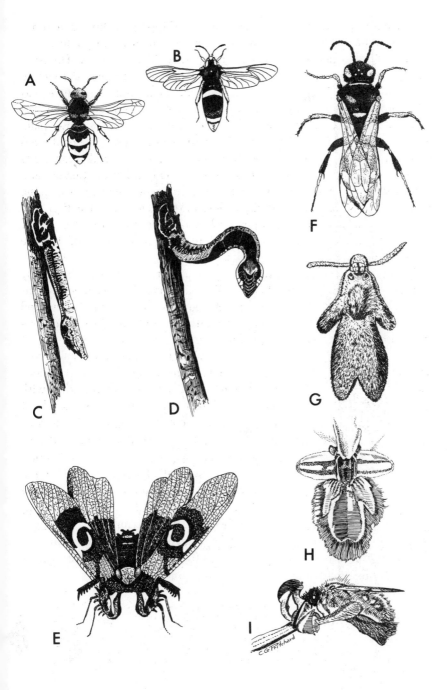

to copulate with these artificial females, bring about pollination (Fig. 1)! A predominance of scents, conspicuous patterns, and colors near the ultraviolet end of the spectrum is typical of butterfly- and bee-pollinated flowers, and is likewise an example of flowers adapting to the sensory capabilities of these animals. Flowers adapted to pollination by such animals as moths, birds, and bats likewise exhibit widely different structural and coloration characteristics that are intricately adapted to the sensory abilities and behavior of the pollinating species.

Although insects are not noted for their learning abilities, they have been proven to exhibit a waning of responses (habituation) to insignificant stimuli and to develop conditioned avoidance or attraction responses as well. Roaches, for example, have been conditioned to associate an electric shock with darkness and thus will reverse their normal negative phototaxis. Honeybees have been trained to associate certain background colors with sugar solutions, and the famous naturalist Karl von Frisch, who discovered the "dances" of honeybees, has been able to train them to distinguish between certain background patterns such as a solid triangle *vs.* an open triangle or a single bar from a double bar.

Even more impressive than these insect capabilities are the results of recent studies on cephalopods such as the octopus (*Octopus vulgaris*). After twenty to thirty trials an octopus is often able to readily distinguish circles from squares, squares from diamonds of the same shape, or horizontal rectangles from erect ones. But if the animal's statocysts are removed it permanently loses its abilities for discriminations involving plane recognition. Likewise, although a normal octopus soon learns to solve problems requiring physical detours, an individual that has been blinded in one eye fails completely in future attempts. The implications of such results in these most "intelligent" of the invertebrates are that the octopus brain relies heavily on stimulus input in regulating appropriate responses, and behavioral flexibility is severely limited. Therefore we must look to the vertebrates to find examples of the highest forms of learning: insight and reasoning.

SUGGESTED READING

Bristowe, W. S., *The World of Spiders*. London: William Collins Sons & Co., Ltd., 1958, 304 pp.

Butler, C. G., "Insect Pheromones." *Biological Reviews* 42:42-87, 1967.

CROMPTON, JOHN, *The Hunting Wasp*. Boston: Houghton Mifflin Company, 1955, 240 pp.

EVANS, H. E., "A Review of Nesting Behavior of Digger Wasps of the Genus *Aphilanthops*, with Special Reference to the Mechanics of Prey Carriage." *Behaviour* 19:239-260, 1962.

FRAENKEL, G. S., and DUNN, D. L., *The Orientation of Animals: Kineses, Taxes, and Compass Reactions*. London: Oxford University Press, 1940, 376 pp.

HIGHNAM, K. C., "Hormones and Behavior in Insects," IN CARTHY, J. C., and DUDDINGTON, C. L. (eds.), *Viewpoints in Biology*, No. 3. London: Butterworth & Co. (Publishers), Ltd., 1964, pp. 219-255.

HINGSTON, R. W. G., *Problem of Instinct and Intelligence*. New York: The Macmillan Company, 1929, 296 pp.

HYMAN, L. H., *The Invertebrates*. New York: McGraw-Hill Book Company, 1940-1959, 5 vols.

JENNINGS, H. S., *Behavior of the Lower Invertebrates*. New York: Columbia University Press, 1906, 366 pp.

MARKL, H., and LINDAUER, M., Physiology of Insect Behavior." IN ROCKSTEIN, MORRIS (ed.), *The Physiology of Insecta*. New York: Academic Press, 1965, Vol. II, pp. 3-122.

ROEDER, K. D., *Nerve Cells and Insect Behavior*. Cambridge, Mass.: Harvard University Press, 1963, 188 pp.

WELLS, M. J., "Invertebrate Learning," *Natural History*, February, 1966, pp. 34-41.

WILSON, E. O., "Pheromones." *Scientific American*, May, 1963, pp. 100-114. (Available in offprint form.)

CHAPTER 4

Vertebrate nervous organization and learning abilities

In passing from the invertebrates to the vertebrates, some major differences in nervous system organization can be seen. In all the vertebrates a dorsal neural tube provides the embryonic basis for the central nervous system, the brain and spinal cord. The relatively simple peripheral nervous system of insects is replaced by one comprised of numerous cranial and spinal nerves serving the extensive system of receptors, muscles, and other effectors that are built around the internal skeleton of the vertebrates. Superimposed on these is a functionally discrete *autonomic system* of sympathetic and parasympathetic nerves that innervate the muscles of the heart and viscera as well as various endocrine and exocrine glands. A complex endocrine system secreting numerous hormones further integrates the metabolism and behavior of vertebrates. The numerous paired and similar spinal nerves indicate that a degree of repetitive segmentation still exists. However, the spinal cord is functionally subordinated to the relatively large brain, in keeping with the trend toward encephalization.

VERTEBRATE BRAIN STRUCTURE AND FUNCTION

Although in the lowest vertebrate the brain is not greatly larger than the adjoining spinal cord, it already exhibits a longitudinal segmentation into lobes that represent fusions of several primitive segments. Through the vertebrate groups these lobes are variably thickened as a result of the closely packed cell bodies of motor, sensory, and association nerves in the outer, or *cortical*, layer of the brain. Connecting these motor and sensory centers are *fiber tracts* comprised largely of axons. Thus, the cortical layer of the advanced vertebrate brain consists of *gray matter* made up largely of neuron cell bodies and nutritive *glial cells,* whereas the myelinated fibers of the inner parts of the brain make up the white matter. This situation is the opposite of that found in the spinal cord, where the cell bodies are limited to the central area within the surrounding white matter.

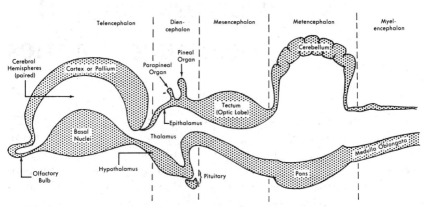

Fig. 2. Diagram of Major Parts of the Vertebrate Brain.

By comparison with invertebrates the vertebrate brain is relatively far larger, providing for a much greater number and complexity of nerve pathways. Further, the vertebrates' myelinated fibers are more efficient in speed of transmission and energy expenditure than are the giant fibers of the larger invertebrates. The smaller diameter of the nerves also provides an opportunity for greatly increasing the total number of sensory and motor nerves, and allows for an almost astronomical number of such fibers.

The *medulla oblongata,* or myelencephalon, is a transition area between brain and spinal cord. The fiber tracts of the spinal cord pass upward (*ascending,* or sensory, tracts) and downward (*descending,* or motor, tracts) through this area as fairly discrete units. But clusters of cell bodies, collectively called *nuclei,* also occur here and serve as local centers of sensory and motor integration. The sensory fiber tracts and nuclei lie dorsal to the motor tracts and nuclei. Between these is the *reticular formation* (or "reticular activating system") of fibers and cell

35

bodies that extends through the entire brain stem. This network is believed to act as an overall regulator of general neural activity, and possibly also activates or inhibits specific nerve pathways as a functional response-monitoring system. Motor controls of the medulla include the musculature of the more posterior primitive gill arches, and thus are involved with swallowing, laryngeal movements, and similar acts. Autonomic reflexes involving heart rate, respiration, secretions of the salivary glands, and arteriole size are also centered here. Sensory information is received by the medulla from several cranial nerves, including the important acoustic nerve.

Lying anterior to the medulla is the area of the brain called the metencephalon, including the pons and the *cerebellum*. The pons is primarily a cerebellar fiber tract area and has only limited motor-control function. The relative development of the dorsal cerebellum is related to the importance of complex motor coordinations. The cerebellum probably evolved as a motor-control center for medulla-received stimuli from the lateral line system and the inner ear, thus providing a basis for equilibrium maintenance. In more advanced and highly active vertebrates such as birds and mammals the cortical surface is considerably thickened, producing an expanded and infolded surface. Although the cerebellum in mammals is evidently sensitive to visual and auditory stimulation, its primary sensory areas are related to proprioception, and its motor areas control associated muscular adjustments affecting posture and equilibrium.

The midbrain, or mesencephalon, is of similar structure throughout the vertebrates but its importance varies greatly in different groups. In lower vertebrates such as fish and amphibians the thickened dorsal tectum receives information from the optic nerve and is the primary integration center of the brain. The *optic lobes* of birds are particularly large, whereas in mammals the cerebral cortex has taken over the midbrain's functions of motor integration and visual sensation, with the latter area serving mainly for motor controls of visual reflexes.

The more anterior diencephalon has three major divisions, the dorsal *epithalamus*, the lateral *thalamus* (and subthalamus), and the ventral *hypothalamus*. The epithalamus includes the parapineal organ, which in some reptiles forms the parietal eye and serves as a photoreceptor. It has been suggested that the similar pineal organ, or epiphysis, which is eyelike in a few vertebrates, may even have some control over sexual activity in mammals. This control possibly occurs through the production of melatonin, which, in turn, may influence the hormonal activity of the gonads or anterior pituitary. Furthermore, it has been suggested that the circadian rhythms of various vertebrate activities may eventually prove to be partly regulated by the pineal organ.

The thalamus appears to be primarily a relay station between the rear portions of the brain and the more anterior centers, with few specific sensory or motor-control centers of its own. On the other hand, the hypothalamus is rich in centers of primary behavioral significance. Besides having such fundamental controls as those regulating body temperature, water balance and appetite, a number of "emotional" motor responses associated with the autonomic nervous system are centered here. These include the acceleration of heart rate, flushing and pallor of the skin, erection of hair or feathers (producing "goosepimples"), sweating and shivering, and modified peristaltic activity. This area and the older parts of the more anterior telencephalon are sometimes called the *limbic system* of the brain; electrical stimulation of different nuclear groups in this region often results in highly specific behavioral patterns which may be alimentary (chewing, swallowing, urinating), defensive, or combative in nature. Sexual reactions (such as penile erections and hypersexuality) may also occur, and "pleasurable" sensations may be initiated. Localized destruction or cuts in this region often lead to strong "emotional" responses. Besides its many neural functions, the hypothalamus produces the hormones released by the posterior lobe of the *pituitary*. Additionally, through the secreting other polypeptides, the hypothalamus influences the production of the numerous anterior pituitary hormones, such as the important *gonadotropins,* which stimulate sexual development and behavior.

The anteriormost telencephalon shows a greatly varied degree of relative development in the vertebrates, but originally evolved in close association with the primitive paired *olfactory bulbs.* Such bulbs are often greatly elongated in the lower vertebrates, but these usually lack marked lateral *cerebral hemispheres.* As the telencephalon increases in size and importance through the vertebrate series, the cerebral hemispheres gradually exceed the olfactory bulbs in size and importance, and finally in mammals a densely packed *neocortical layer* of cell bodies (the *neopallium*) covers the entire dorsal and lateral surface of the forebrain, nearly obscuring both the olfactory bulbs and the midbrain. Thus, the increasingly convoluted *cerebral cortex* eventually comes to dominate the mammalian nervous system, reaching its culmination of size and thickness in the primates. The cerebral hemispheres of man comprise more than three-fourths of the total weight of the brain. Although both birds and reptiles have moderately large cerebral hemispheres, there is only a rudimentary cortical layer present, and the hemispheres are smooth and largely made up of fiber tracts to and from the large basal nuclei.

Although the anterior olfactory centers dominate the telencephalon in the lower vertebrates, these are gradually subordinated in size and functional significance as the lateral cerebral hemispheres evaginate and enlarge through increases in the number of sensory and motor fibers and the thickening of the cortical layer of cell bodies. Many of these fibers are *association neurons,* which connect various parts of each cerebral hemisphere, and other *commissural fibers* make transverse connections between the two hemispheres. Finally, *projection fibers* connect the cerebrum with other parts of the brain and so allow for feedback of sensory and motor information from these areas.

In mammals, at least, there have been found *modality-specific* sensory areas on the cerebral cortex for olfaction, vision, hearing, taste, and temperature sensations. An anatomically specific area, or *somatotopic* relationship between body configuration and cortex surface area, has also been found for a number of mammals, including man. It is therefore possible to "map out" on the brain surface centers of touch reception by noting the electrical activity of the brain initiated when different body surface areas are stimulated. In this manner *sensory figurines* (or "homunculi") can be plotted in which body regions are represented by points on the cortex surface, but with areas of particular sensory importance to the species (muzzle of dog, thumb of primates) much enlarged relative to their actual proportions. Similarly, motor areas of the cortex are somatotopically organized and point stimulation of these areas can be used to demonstrate the presence of a *motor figurine* just anterior to the sensory figurine. Smaller supplemental motor and sensory areas have been found in a number of mammals and also are somatotopically organized. Although in most mammals these *sensorimotor areas* and the sensory areas for vision, olfaction and hearing cover most of the cortex, in man and the manlike apes considerable portions of the cerebral cortex are "silent" with respect to motor control or sensory stimulation. These *association areas* are believed to be the anatomical site of neural function involved in memory and learning.

Individual memories, or *engrams,* are believed to have a molecular basis. It is thought that memory is a two-stage process, with the first stage temporary, perhaps lasting an hour or so, whereas the second stage is a permanent *memory trace,* imprinted in the central nervous system at a conscious or subconscious level. A number of theories to account for learning and memory have been advanced. These have usually involved the formation of new neural interconnections, the permanent physiological or anatomical modification of existing synaptic pathways, or biochemical changes in the neurons themselves. Recent evidence strongly implicates RNA in the learning and memory process. It has been learned that stimulation of brain cells results in an increase in RNA in these cells, and that conditioned mammals show increased levels of RNA in cortical cells. Injection of ribonuclease into cats interferes with memory and sensory discrimination, whereas injection of RNA into rats has reportedly shortened conditioning time and lengthened the time to extinction of conditioned responses.

Dr. Holger Hyden has hypothesized that the structure of RNA, in particular its base sequence, can be altered and perhaps made more stable by the electrical activity of the neuron producing it. This RNA may then specify the construction of specific protein molecules which in turn may affect the secretion rate of transmitter substances. According to this theory the same neuron could participate in different synaptic pathways with differential sensitivity, since the various proteins produced by the RNA under different stimulations would each be specific to certain modulated frequencies of electrical activity.

SIMPLER LEARNED RESPONSES

All levels of learned behavior can be demonstrated in the vertebrates. When a cat is behaviorally habituated to a pure tone, it may be shown that neural activity in the suprasylvian gyrus, as measured by an electroencephalograph, changes from the "arousal" state to the slow-wave pattern typical of sleeping animals. However, an exposure to a different sound frequency (1,000 vs. 500 cps) will produce arousal, as will a new stimulus when presented nearly simultaneously with the sound to which the animal has been habituated.

A second type of simple learned behavior is imprinting, which was first demonstrated in birds but also has been described for fish and mammals. The early observations of Oskar Heinroth and Konrad Lorenz on goslings suggested that a special kind of learning may occur in the newly hatched birds which (1) was relatively permanent and irreversible and (2) was limited to a short *critical* (or "sensitive") *period* soon after hatching. At this time social attachments may be formed that will persist in later life, particularly at the time of mating. Thus, although the young will normally be imprinted on their parents at this time, under experimental conditions it is possible to imprint the animals on foster parents or even inanimate objects.

The usual test of imprinting is the relative tendency of the young to follow the object on which they have been imprinted, a response termed the *following reaction*. Although it has been suggested that the strength of this imprinting may be directly related to the amount of energy expended in its initial following during imprinting ("law of effort"), this idea does not appear to be of general application. Reasons for the termination of the critical period, after which imprinting becomes impossible, are still uncertain. It is probably not the result of a simple maturational end to sensitivity, since it can be extended considerably in the absence of any stimulation that might produce imprinting. More probably it represents a gradual development of timidity, or the end of a state of "low anxiety."

Recent work with waterfowl has suggested that simple imprinting, as measured by the following reaction, should be distinguished from sexual imprinting, or the effects of early experience on subsequent mate selection. The sensitive period for the latter is much longer (several weeks *vs.* a few days), and may differ in the two sexes. Male mallards (*Anas platyrhynchos*) can be sexually imprinted on the other species of waterfowl by rearing them with foster mothers, and will even imprint on other males, forming homosexual attachments that will last for years, even in the presence of available females. However, female mallards reared in the same manner are never affected, and instead continue to react properly to the male mallards during pair formation, evidently through an innate recognition of male mallard plumages. In nondimorphic species of ducks the sexes are apparently equally susceptible to sexual imprinting. Finally, it has been found that sexual imprinting is more readily achieved in ducklings using a foster mother than by rearing them with foster siblings.

Although it is less easy to prove the existence of imprinting in species having altricial young which require prolonged parental care, as is true of most birds and mammals, it is well known that early learning may have important effects in later social life. In particular, habituation rates may be prolonged in mammals exposed to subnormal stimulation as infants. Monkeys raised in isolation exhibit abnormal sexual behavior as adults and nearly always are unable to mate successfully. The importance of early experience in shaping the adult behavior of human beings still remains to be completely assessed but should not be underestimated.

Conditioning is a form of associative learning that is well demonstrated in vertebrates. Both *classical conditioning*, in which the animal has no control over the stimulation, and *instrumental conditioning*, in which the animal is able to influence the onset or type of stimulus through its own activity, were first worked out with mammalian subjects. In both types of conditioning the animal learns to make new associations and thus modifies its responses to various combinations of stimuli. Conditioning offers a splendid means of testing the sensory discrimination and motor abilities of animals, and also enables one to test rates of conditioning (or subsequent extinction of the conditioned response) in different animals or in different situations. However, it is difficult to estimate how important conditioning may be as a general learning mechanism under natural conditions.

The basis for instrumental, or "operant," conditioning lies in the subject's capacity for recognizing the different effects of its own activities, and encountering through trial and error the combination of activities that produce a desirable result, such as a reward, or avoidance of a noxious situation. In all likelihood a generalized form of such *trial and error learning* plays a most important role in the life of many vertebrates, from the gradual learning of suitable foods to the recognition of individual social partners. For example, European red squirrels (*Sciurus vulgaris*) instinctively recognize nuts as a source of food and manipulate them readily, but only through experience do they gradually learn to crack the shells efficiently. Likewise, various species of captive finches will at first accept a wide range of seeds indiscriminantly, but gradually learn to prefer the largest that their bills are adapted to crushing. Although birds in general have an innate nest-building capacity, it is frequently found that the quality of nest construction improves with succeeding attempts. This might be the result of trial and error learning or, possibly, late maturational changes in motor abilities.

Commonly used tests for trial and error learning abilities include *maze problems*, which force the animal to achieve an ultimate goal that at the outset, at least, is not visible to it. The animal must randomly attempt various solutions to the problem unil it finds a combination that is successful. Its ability in future attempts to substitute the proper solution for the random attempts is used as a measure of trial and error learning. *Detour problems* are generally regarded as more difficult because they require the animal to take an indirect pathway to a desirable and visible goal. Unlike classical conditioning, in which additional or substitute responses are developed, trial and error learning involves the subtraction of various nonrewarding responses after trying them and determining that they are ineffectual, until finally only rewarding responses are performed. Furthermore, unlike classical conditioning, the motor patterns are appetitive inasmuch as they must precede the reinforcement of a successful completion of the problem rather than being performed as a result of a stimulus controlled by the experimenter.

There is evidence for trial and error learning in all major groups of vertebrates. Fish have proven adept at "place learning," or learning to anticipate the appearance of food in a certain location. Goldfish have been taught simple mazes, and many fish have been shown capable of mastering various detour problems in order to reach food. Salamanders and newts have learned T mazes or zigzag mazes, and turtles have been able to master mazes with as many as six blind alleys. Pigeons (*Columbia livia*) have also eventually been able to learn mazes with six blind alleys; additionally, the birds remembered the solution over a six week rest period. William Thorpe has thoroughly summarized these and other experiments on learning abilities in nonmammalian vertebrates as well as invertebrates, and extensive work on mammalian learning abilities has been performed by psychologists, particularly on laboratory rodents.

Although birds undoubtedly rely heavily on instinctive patterns for many of their activities, they have also been found to exhibit somewhat surprising learning abilities. Impressive examples of these are the experiments of Nicholas Pastore, who has proven that canaries (*Serinus canarius*) can be taught to discriminate a *unique* object out of a group of nine, the other eight being identical in all characteristics. This discrimination was achieved for four birds after an average of 160 trials, by which time the criterion of fifteen proper choices out of twenty attempts was reached. With subsequent consecutive but differing versions of the problem the average number of trials to attain this criterion rapidly dropped to less than thirty by the tenth problem, indicating both a profiting from past experience wih related problems and a capacity to recognize "uniqueness" in groups of objects. This kind of experiment tests the application of previous solutions to similar but new problems, an ability for which birds are not held in high regard.

A sense of unnamed numbers, either simultaneous (requiring a discrimination within a group of differently numbered objects) or successive (requiring the recognition of an unnumbered object in a sequential series) has also been demonstrated in birds. For example, ravens (*Corvus corax*) have been taught to select one box (out of five) having the same number of irregularly placed spots as a key pattern. To prove the presence of a successive number sense, a jackdaw (*Corvus monedula*) was trained to open black boxes until it obtained two rewards, green boxes until it had three, red until it had four, and white until it had five! Although these experiments prove a remarkable avian prelinguistic sense of uniqueness and unnamed numbers, which presumably have no immediate survival value to birds, it is debatable whether the learning abilities illustrating these perceptual capacities represent anything more impressive than trial and error learning, as suggested by the large number of trials required to attain a convincing criterion in such experiments.

ADVANCED PROBLEM-SOLVING PROCESSES

The most efficient method of problem-solving consists of abandoning random trial and error responses to a problem in favor of a directed or "calculated" solution to it. Such an apprehension of relationships, or "sudden adaptive reorganization of experience" (Thorpe), is called *insight* learning. Although examples of insight behavior in birds, fish and even insects have been proposed, these usually fail to be convincing. For example, tool usage has been suggested as a case of insight behavior, and, indeed, a few cases of regular tool use among insects (*e.g.*, the pebble-pounding by *Ammophila*) are known. But these examples are species-specific segments of larger instinctive patterns that, although remarkable, can be readily explained by natural selection. Similarly, one can find instances of species-specific tool usage by birds (the "paintbrush" of the satin bower bird, *Ptilonorhynchus violaceus*, and the cactus probe of the Galapagos woodpecker-finch, *Camarhynchus pallidus*), which likewise are clearly highly adaptive instinctive patterns.

Experimentally, *detour problems* and complex *delayed response* problems are sometimes used as tests for insight learning but must be considered carefully with respect to their relation to the animal's normal activities. For example, fish have been able to master some fairly complex detour problems. A European minnow (*Phoxinus laevis*) is able eventually to swim around U-shaped detours to reach a bait but does not exhibit a sudden solution indicating insightful learning. Likewise, birds which obtain their food in flight might be expected to perform more poorly in maze problems than would ground foragers, and water-fowl are notoriously poor at solving terrestrial detour problems.

Delayed-response problems are those in which the animal must re-spond properly at some time after the appropriate stimulus has been presented and removed. The length of time that the animal is able to delay its response is taken as a measure of its symbolic capacities. However, many other factors may be important here, such as the organism's general activity level, its susceptibility to distracting stimuli, and its capacity for one-trial learning. The female digger wasp's ability to delay her provisioning of several nests for several hours, based on a single observational visit in the morning, is a case of one-trial learning associated with a greatly delayed response.

Complex problem solving which requires a regular *alternation* of responses (right, left, right, left) or a *double alternation* (right, right left, left) has also been used as a measure of higher learning capacities. Many mammals can readily learn single-alternation problems, but only a few are capable of learning a double-alternation problem of any length. Cats, dogs, and racoons have been able to master LLRR se-quences, but rarely can they extend the series beyond four choice points. By combining alternation problems with delayed responses a greater degree of complexity can be achieved. Pigeons have proven able to perform better than chance with an enforced ten-second delay between single alternation responses, and show better than 75 per cent accuracy with delays of five seconds or less.

Many problems designed to test for higher learning abilities require the formulation of an abstract *concept,* such as uniqueness or oddity. Unlike the situation described for birds earlier, monkeys soon profit from exposure to different oddity problems to the point where one-trial learning occurs, suggesting a total insight into the principle of the prob-lem. It is even possible to train monkeys to respond to an odd *color* when all are presented on a particular background and to an odd *form* when the same objects are presented on a different background. Such learning is a type of *conditional reaction,* in which the proper response varies under different conditions. For example, monkeys have been trained to select blue objects from a mixed group of red and blue objects under one stimulus, whereas with a different stimulus they will select the red ones. Only primates are regularly successful at this kind of problem. This ability of primates to grasp the essential principle behind differ-ent but related problems, thus reducing trials to successful completion of subsequent problems, has been called a *learning set* and appears to be fairly closely correlated with cerebral development in the primate series. As such it probably comes closer to measuring *reasoning* capabilities than do any other types of learning problems.

ENDOCRINE INTEGRATION OF VERTEBRATE BEHAVIOR

With the vertebrates' increasingly flexible and complex response capabilities, the vexing problems of "motivations" and "drives" must be taken into account. Although these too must have some kind of physiological basis, they are difficult to account for or to attempt to measure. It has been mentioned that the motor centers of such "motivated" behavior pattern as attack, escape, and alimentary and sexual responses are largely centered in the region of the hypothalamus and adjacent "limbic system." The close anatomical connections between the hypothalamus and the pituitary gland suggest that endocrine activity may play an important role in regulating motivated responses, and microinjections of gonadal hormones into the hypothalamus of rats has produced spectacular behavioral effects.

The influence of hormones on sexual behavior in vertebrates is now well recognized. In birds, for example, the gonadal hormones (estradiol, testosterone, and progesterone) and, indirectly, the anterior pituitary gonadotropins are known to be highly significant in regulating reproductive behavior patterns. This latter group of hormones includes follicle-stimulating hormone (FSH), luteinizing hormone (LH or ICSH), and prolactin (LTH). Furthermore, not only may the secretion of such hormones affect behavior, but also behavior may influence the secretion of hormones. In female cats, weasels, and rabbits, for example, copulation will trigger the hormonal changes that cause ovulation, and in several birds the sight of a nest constructed by the male serves as a stimulus for secreting the pituitary hormones regulating ovulation in females. The gonadal hormones testosterone and estradiol greatly affect sexual responses, as proven by injection of these hormones into immature birds or by removing their sources in adult birds. Testosterone also influences dominance and general aggressiveness, and stimulates male vocalizations. Surprisingly, the courtship behavior and bright plumages of female phalaropes, in which there is a sexual reversal of pair-formation behavior and relative plumage brightness, is also under the control of testosterone secreted by the ovaries. Parental responses, such as the brooding of eggs and care of the young, are generally controlled by prolactin and progesterone in birds.

The importance of hormones in regulating sexual behavior undoubtedly extends throughout the vertebrate series; pituitary gonadotropins have been found in all the vertebrate classes. In lampreys these are known to time reproduction and to affect gamete production and release, but the degree of pituitary control is less complete than in more advanced groups. Both of the gonadotropic hormones, follicle-stimulating hormone and luteinizing hormone, occur in all the tetrapods, and at least the latter also occurs in the jawed fishes. Pituitary control of courtship behavior is indicated for some fish such as gobies (*Bathygobius*), and prolactin possibly regulates parental behavior in wrasse (*Crenilabrus*). It has been suggested that the reproduction of primitive vertebrates originally was environmentally controlled through stimulating the secretion of neurosecretory products of the hypothalamus, and later the anterior pituitary provided an endocrine link between the hypothalamus and the gonads, presumably increasing the degree of "feedback" control and serving as an integrating mechanism.

Recent work on canaries by the English ethologist Robert Hinde has demonstrated beautifully the significance of both internal factors (hormonal and neural interactions) and external factors (day length, presence of mate, nest materials) in providing for an orderly sequence of behavioral events from the beginning of sexual activity in spring through incubation. For example, females injected with estradiol will begin to build a nest of grass and similar materials, but the completion of a functional nest depends on the presence of a brood patch. This vascularized and featherless area of the abdomen results from prolactin secretion that is stimulated in part by the presence of a sexually active male. The sensitive tactile receptors of the brood patch stimulate the female to line the nest with soft feathers, bringing it to completion just prior to the laying of the first egg. The interaction of these numerous factors ensures that the important reproductive cycle will not be initiated in a situation that would be inappropriate and unsuccessful, such as the wrong time of year, absence of mate, or lack of nest site and materials.

SUGGESTED READING

BARNETT, S. A., *A Study of Behavior*. London: Methuen & Co., Ltd., 1963, 288 pp.

HARLOW, H. F., and HARLOW, M. K., "Learning to Think." *Scientific American*, August, 1949, pp. 36-39. (Available in offprint form.)

Hess, E. H., "'Imprinting' in Animals." *Scientific American*, March, 1958, pp. 81-90. (Available in offprint form.)

Hinde, R., "Temporal Relations of Brood Patch Development in Domesticated Canaries." *Ibis* 104:90-97, 1962.

Holst, E. von and Saint Paul, U. von, "Electrically Controlled Behavior." *Scientific American*, March, 1962, pp. 50-59. (Available in offprint form.)

Hyden, Holger, "Satellite Cells in the Nervous System." *Scientific American*, December, 1961, pp. 62-70. (Available in offprint form.)

Olds, James, "Pleasure Centers in the Brain." *Scientific American*, October, 1956, pp. 105-116. (Available in offprint form.)

Pastore, N. "Further Experiments in Counting Ability: Canaries and Mynas." *Zeitschrift für Tierpsychologie* 19:665-686, 1962.

Thorpe, W. H., *Learning and Instinct in Animals*, 2nd. ed. London: Methuen & Co., 1963, 558 pp.

Wooldridge, D. E., *The Machinery of the Brain*. New York: McGraw-Hill Paperbacks, 1963, 252 pp.

CHAPTER 5

Ontogeny of vertebrate behavior

One of the important precepts in zoology is the principle that ontogeny recapitulates phylogeny in the embryonic development of anatomical structures. Since behavior is a reflection of anatomy, it might be expected that a similar situation would pertain, thus partially accounting for progressive behavioral changes during the development of an individual. Ontogenetic behavior changes appear, however, to be the result of two primary variables, maturational development of inherited responses on the one hand, and, on the other, behavioral changes resulting from experience, including both self-learning through repetition and learning through association with others. The problem of separating "innate" from "acquired" patterns is therefore a doubly difficult one, for not only may basically instinctive patterns be modified through physical maturation and experience, but also learning abilities are dependent upon the inheritance of certain sensory and motor capacities, or even on inherited "predispositions to learn." Furthermore, although an animal can often be raised in isolation from others, it cannot be separated from itself, and thus self-learning may still be possible.

ONTOGENY OF MOTOR PATTERNS

It is convenient to consider the time of birth (in viviparous animals) or hatching (in oviparous species) as the starting point in the ontogeny of behavior, but there is also an embryology of behavior which may occur in the egg or parent during which reflexes may be "practiced" and a certain degree of self-learning is possible. In precocial birds, vocalizations may actually begin a day or two prior to hatching, and such unhatched birds will respond to the warning call of the mother by becoming quiet.

After birth or hatching the acquisition of new behavior patterns follows one of several patterns. A common one is a gradual *differentiation* of behavior that parallels the structural differentiation of organs and organ systems, with generalized body movements gradually giving way to more complex and specific motor patterns. But other behavior patterns may appear fully developed the first time they are elicited, either serving a functional purpose at that time or gradually being incorporated into other responses to form an adaptive pattern. In the first three or four post-hatching days of the European cuckoo (*Cuculus canorus*), the blind young exhibit a remarkable reflex response, in that they will eject from the nest any solid object with which they come into contact. Thus, other nestlings or eggs will soon be removed from the nest, leaving only a single cuckoo to be reared. Likewise, the African honey-guides (*Indicator* spp.), which are also brood parasites, show a similar nestling response in that the newly hatched young fiercely attack other nestlings with their sharply hooked beaks, eventually killing them. The stabbing reflex wanes and the sharp tips of the beak drop off in a few weeks, after having served their lethal purpose.

As new behavior patterns emerge, through gradual differentiation or sudden appearance, they may be incorporated into more complex chains of responses. A common phenomenon is for these chains to develop in *additive* fashion, with the segments of the chain appearing in progressive sequence until a functional response has been developed. The gradual development of feeding and locomotory responses in nestling passerine birds provides such an example. Alternatively, component parts of complex patterns, not of immediate functional value, may appear in *independent*, nonconsecutive fashion, only later to be organized into adaptive patterns. In studying the ontogeny of pintail (*Anas acuta*) ducklings, Robert Smith found that three basic head postures plus a "pump" movement occur in young fledglings, especially during crowding. Some of these postures are later incorporated into various displays performed by adults during pair formation, and occur as parts of these rigidly stereotyped postures.

Recent studies of jungle fowl (*Gallus gallus*), the undomesticated ancestor of domestic fowl, also indicate that adult sexual and agonistic behavior patterns gradually develop ontogenetically at varying rates until they come to have adaptive function. Thus, overt escape behavior is manifested shortly after hatching by various strong stimuli. Aggressive behavior begins to appear within a few days and gradually becomes directed toward other individuals. Within three weeks kicking and pecking responses are added to the aggressive hopping and wing-flapping, and fighting becomes more intense. Between the third and the seventh week the attack and escape patterns begin to show simultaneous elicitation, resulting in various irrelevant motor patterns that include ground-pecking and preening, possibly representing *redirected* movements, in that the activated motor pattern is directed to an object other than that which stimulated it. During the next five weeks other irrelevant motor responses occur during fighting, apparently representing ambivalent or compromise combinations of attack and escape, and producing "side display" and "waltzing" postures that later serve as the basis for these male sexual displays. Two additional precursors of sexual displays appear after twelve weeks; these are "tidbitting" and "nesting," which appear to be the result of motor patterns produced by the simultaneous elicitation of attack, escape, and sexual tendencies. When the birds are reared in isolation this normal social development is prevented, and, although many of the displays may develop, they may be directed abnormally. Males isolated for the entire first year are never able to develop normal sexual behavior.

The maturation of behavioral patterns of reproductive significance are frequently under hormonal control, and endocrine levels rather than differentiation of neural pathways or effector structures may be crucial in timing the initial appearance of these patterns. By injecting downy male ducklings of several species with testosterone, precocial movements, postures, and calls can be elicited which are typical of adult males of the species during pair formation. Females treated with testosterone, however, do not show these responses. Such results suggest that in these birds, at least, no self-learning or physical maturation in a social situation is necessary for the elicitation of male sexual responses. It has also been found that the sexual differences in the micturation behavior of adult dogs are under hormonal control, with the male pattern gradually developing under the influence of testosterone, whereas the female retains the juvenile pattern. Injection of this hormone in male puppies results in a precocious assumption of the adult pattern, but early castration of males produces a retention of the juvenile behavior pattern.

A comparison of the acquisition of seasonally elicited behavior patterns with the development of normal growth and maturational responses is of some interest. In nestlings of the European cormorant

(*Phalacrocorax carbo*) the first elements to appear are usually those at the end of a behavioral sequence, or consummatory acts, whereas the earlier appetitive elements may appear later in retrogressive fashion. However, during the seasonal development of reproductive patterns in adults there tends to be a progressive or additive acquisition of behavioral elements. These may first appear in rudimentary or incomplete form, when they are termed *intention movements.* Intention movements are frequently the motor basis for displays that convey the individual's motivation in advance. Such displays may integrate the activities of a social unit or allow a substitution of *ritualized fighting* for actual encounters.

IMPRINTING AND EARLY EXPERIENCE

It is clear that early experiences may have much more marked effects on adult behavior patterns than has been previously appreciated. Thus, the concept of critical or sensitive periods of learning must be extended beyond those species known to exhibit classic "imprinting," as discussed in the previous chapter, to a much wider range of species and of behavior patterns. There are three principal means of testing the significance of early experience. First, one may expose the animal to enhanced or enriched stimulation of a general nature (social contacts, opportunities for motor activity, auditory or visual stimulation) or a specific type (song patterns of adults, for example). Secondly, one may deprive the animal of stimulation during one or more stages of ontogeny by rearing it in varying degrees of isolation ("Kasper Hauser" experiments). Finally, one may alter the stimulation to which the animal might normally be exposed during development and determine its possible effects on behavior. Examples of the latter include attempts to imprint animals on other than normal parental stimuli, or exposing naive birds to song types of other species. In experiments with mallard ducklings, a variety of objects have served as mother substitutes. Of a group of five ducklings imprinted on a decoy model (painted like a male mallard) for twenty-four hours, all preferred this model to adult female mallards with broods their age. There has also been limited success in imprinting ducklings on a model associated with the recorded calls of males (which normally do not attend the broods), but Gilbert Gottlieb has shown that naive ducklings have a greater tendency to follow the recorded calls of adult females of their own than of other species, suggesting an innate predisposition for proper parental recognition during imprinting.

Psychologists have found that rats which spend their early lives in isolated laboratory cages tend to be relatively poorly adapted to new situations, but those which have received considerable handling or exposure to stress stimuli (electric shocks) show better than average adaptation to these situations as adults. In monkeys, early social contacts with other infants are vital to the establishment of normal adult social relations. Monkeys raised alone in cages from the first six months to a year have generally proven incapable of normal adult sexual behavior. When denied real mothers, infant monkeys will accept primitive surrogate mother figures made of wire and cloth, but greatly prefer a soft cloth-covered form to an open wire model. Evidently physical contact between the infant and mother is vitally important in the normal social development of infant primates.

As a means of separating strictly instinctive patterns from those which are dependent upon learning experiences in the presence of other individuals, isolation experiments are necessary. The dangers of possibly obtaining abnormal behavior patterns resulting from lack of social contacts are in this case outweighed by the advantages of being able to control carefully the timing and degree of various types of stimulation. A great deal of work of this kind has been done with birds, particularly with regard to the ontogeny of vocalizations.

Vocalizations of birds have been broadly divided into "calls" and "songs." Calls are short, relatively simple signals with little individual variation in sound pattern, and may be uttered by either or both sexes at various times during the year. Thus, they are the basic "language" of birds, by which important categories of information are exchanged among individuals in a relatively uniform way. These are present in most birds reared under individual isolation, although in some cases particular calls have failed to develop. It is not surprising that bird calls are relatively free of learning influences, since one criterion of a good communication system is wide understandability, free of local dialects or variations in meaning. These calls of songbirds are usually developed by the end of the first three months following hatching, although some are dependent for expression on the hormones associated with reproduction.

Songs of birds are normally distinguished from calls by their generally more complex acoustic structure, and are especially typical of the male (rarely the female) during courtship and territorial defense. Songs may be somewhat arbitrarily divided into the "primary song" typical of males in full reproductive condition and two development stages of primary song. The first of these is "subsong," which may consist of a mixture of calls and somewhat random, subdued warbling with little if any apparent patterning. By the end of the first autumn the subsong is usually replaced by "rehearsed song" in which a definite patterning of notes suggestive of primary song can be detected. Most female passerines (a group that includes all the "songbirds") do not exhibit either rehearsed song or primary song. Males of various species of higher passerines reared in individual isolation are usually capable of developing a kind of primary song having species-typical elements but which is usually a good deal simpler in acoustical structure than "normal" primary song. A hand-reared chaffinch (*Fringilla coelebs*) will produce a song of about the proper length, number of notes, and nearly normal acoustic frequency. However, the song lacks the finer song details, the typical three-part division of chaffinch primary song, and also lacks a terminal flourish. When several isolated birds are raised together, more complex songs are produced which are very similar in all the sibling birds but which also may be quite different from the typical chaffinch song. If the young birds have an opportunity to hear some chaffinch song in the wild before being isolated, but are isolated before they begin to sing much, the three-parted song and terminal flourish will appear, and a nearly typical chaffinch primary song is produced. This result suggests that primary song in chaffinches depends both on an innate substrate and on a learned element that allows for a certain individual variation within a broader range of species-specificity. The "sensitive period" during which the juveniles may learn parts of their individual songs from others usually does not last beyond the first winter. By this time each male will have developed a song that is individually separable from its conspecifics, but which still fits into the general "mold" of the species, thus allowing both for individual recognition and species recognition.

When male songbirds are reared in isolation from conspecifics but are allowed to hear other species, two possible results may occur. In some species such as the chaffinch a "hybrid repertoire" of learned motifs and species-typical motifs will emerge. Alternatively, a completely "borrowed repertoire" may develop, combining song elements from all species the individual may have heard during its sensitive period. Some species are adept at learning alien songs, even under conditions encountered in the wild; these birds are commonly called "mimics." This capacity for vocal imitation or, more properly, *vocal mimesis*, has been a source of considerable speculation and wonder. In

America the mockingbird (*Mimus polyglottos*) and other "mimic thrushes" exhibit this capability, and the Australian lyrebird (*Menura*) is an even more remarkable mimic. One suggestion as to the function of such interspecific mimicry is that perhaps most other birds are repelled from the territory of a competent mimic, thus reducing competition for food or other habitat needs.

INNATE PREDISPOSITIONS FOR LEARNING

Although mockingbirds and other mimics are highly flexible in their vocalizations, there is no evidence that they are more readily able to learn nonvocal motor responses than are other birds. This capacity for being able to acquire certain responses through experience but being unable to modify other aspects of behavior has been called *localized learning*. Niko Tinbergen has reported that it requires herring gulls (*Larus argentatus*) about five days to learn to recognize their young, which they must protect from other gulls. During the first five days it is possible to substitute other similar young without recognition on the part of the adults, but if it is done any later, the adults will neglect or kill them. On the other hand, gulls have a much reduced capacity for recognition of their own eggs and evidently possess only the most limited basis for recognition of eggs. By experimental work with models, in which the incubating gull must "choose" between several types of egg models variously sized, patterned, and shaped, it has been found that spotted eggs are preferred to plain eggs (gull eggs are spotted), rounded models are preferred to sharp-edged ones, and big eggs are preferred to small ones, even if the larger model is twenty times the size of a normal egg! Thus, a gull is likely to try to incubate one or more enormous artificial eggs in preference to its own eggs under such conditions. Such larger-than-life stimuli are called *supernormal* (or superoptimal) releasers and result from the summation of various stimulus components, producing a total stimulus value greater than that encountered under normal conditions.

Tinbergen has distinguished from localized learning a very similar manifestation of an innate disposition for learning which he has called *preferential learning*. This concerns differential capabilities for modifying responses to various stimuli in the environment. In herring gulls, for example, incubating birds will respond more strongly to the nest site than to the eggs themselves, and will return to an empty nest when the eggs have been removed from it and placed a foot or so away. It would appear that only certain aspects of the environment may be used by the bird when it learns its nest location, while others, sometimes more obvious to humans, may be ignored. The learning of conspecific rather than alien primary song motifs by birds is also an example of preferential learning. Thus, bluebirds (*Sialia sialis*) reared by James Hartshorne in sound isolation from prehatching to the age of six months did not respond to recordings of the primary songs of the American robin (*Turdus migratorius*), wood thrush (*Hylocichla mustelina*), or Baltimore oriole (*Icterus galbula*) to each of which they were exposed once. However, they showed apparent interest in a recording of bluebird primary song when it was played backward. After it was played forward they sang a crude version of it in less than a minute, and much improved versions within five minutes!

The transition from birth or hatching in mammals and birds to integration into relatively permanent and highly structured social grouping is a gradual one, but it is useful to consider the process as one comprised of a number of phases. Nicholas Collias has suggested that six fairly distinct stages of social development exist for birds and mammals. The earliest consists of an *initial predisposition to respond* in various ways, such as pecking, sucking, following, or performing other simple responses. Then follows a *period of self-reinforcement* of those initial responses which are in some way rewarding. Next, there is a phase of gradually *increasing social discrimination*, producing, for example, the development of "peck orders" of dominant and subordinant individuals, based on the recognition of individual differences. There also develops a tendency toward *socialization guided by family bonds,* as foraging habits, antipredator responses, and other important responses are acquired through familial associations. However, the young animals usually exhibit *increasing social independence with age,* ultimately causing the disruption of family bonds and a *reintegration into new social groups.* Behavioral characteristics of these social aggregations will be considered next.

SUGGESTED READING

COLLIAS, N. E., "Social Development in Birds and Mammals." In BLISS, E. L. (ed.), *Roots of Behavior,* New York: Harper & Bros., 1962, pp. 264-273.
DENENBERG, V. H., "Early Experience and Emotional Development." Scientific American, June, 1963, pp. 138-146. (Available in offprint form.)
DIAMOND, N., "A Critical Evaluation of the Ontogeny of Human Sexual Behavior. *Quarterly Review of Biology* 40:147-175, 1965.

Fabricius, E., "Crucial Periods in the Development of the Following Response in Young Nidifugous Birds." *Zeitschrift für Tierpsychologie* 21:326-337, 1964.

Harlow, H. F., "Love in Infant Monkeys." *Scientific American*, June, 1959, pp. 68-74. (Available in offprint form.)

———, and Harlow, M. K., "Social Deprivation in Monkeys." *Scientific American*, November, 1962, pp. 136-146. (Available in offprint form.)

Lanyon, W. E., "The Ontogeny of Vocalization in Birds." In Lanyon, W. E. and Tavolga, W. N. (eds.), *Animal Sounds and Communication*, Pub. No. 7, American Institute of Biological Sciences. Washington, D. C.: American Institute of Biological Sciences, 1960, pp. 321-327.

Sluckin, W., *Imprinting and Early Learning.* Chicago: Aldine Publishing Company, 1965, 147 pp.

Thorpe, W. H., "The Ontogeny of Behavior." In Moore, J. A. (ed.), *Ideas in Modern Biology.* Garden City, N. Y.: Natural History Press, 1965, 563 pp.

CHAPTER 6

Social
behavior

One of the characteristics of living organisms is that populations of particular species are not randomly scattered but usually occur in clumped aggregations. At the lowest level these might be aggregations of cells only, as may exist in colonial protozoans. More typically, they are intraspecific aggregations of individuals that have clustered together as a result of attraction to a common ecological situation, or to one another. The sessile "beds" of marine mollusks, barnacles, and other relatively fixed individuals may thus result from attraction of motile larval forms to a common suitable substrate, and the more mobile aggregations (flocks, herds, schools, colonies, and the like) of vertebrates and invertebrates are more typical examples of social groupings. Similar interspecific aggregations of two or more species may be produced by random mixing or may result from positive interaction of benefit to one or both participants. Thus, we may recognize such interspecific social interactions as unilaterally beneficial *commensalism* and *social parasitism,* and situations grading into bilaterally beneficial *mutualism,* which may be either facultative ("protocooperation") or obligate (true mutualistic "symbiosis"). Other intraspecific responses, if not actually involving overt cooperation, may reduce or prevent actual fighting (agonistic behavior), may facilitate fertilization (reproductive behavior), or may increase the chances for survival of the next generation (parental behavior). Some specific examples of these categories of primarily intraspecific social interactions will now be considered.

AGONISTIC BEHAVIOR

Agonistic behavior patterns are those which include all types of primarily hostile responses ranging from overt attack to overt escape. In ethological terms, such behavior results from variations in the actual and relative tendencies of an animal to attack and escape. It is assumed that these tendencies increase and decrease independently of one another and of sexual tendencies, allowing for an almost infinite range of internal states. When attack and escape tendencies are aroused but sexual tendencies remain unimportant, nonreproductive fighting may ensue. This often occurs in situations of a restricted food source, as at feeding stations or other places where animals must come into close contact during foraging. When no dominance hierarchy exists among the participants, actual fighting may result. Frequently, as during periods of reproduction, sexual tendencies are simultaneously aroused with attack and escape tendencies, possibly producing reproductive fighting among individuals of the same sex or even between sexes. Such a waste of energy during the critical period of reproduction is highly deleterious, and various substitutes for actual fighting have been evolved in many species. Perhaps the foremost of these is *territoriality.*

Territoriality results in a restriction of fighting to a limited area (either a fixed topographic area or, occasionally, a mobile area around the mate). It was first described for birds but is now known to occur in a number of other vertebrates, including certain mammals, fish, and reptiles. Besides the obvious values of reducing fighting, territoriality also results in a spacing out that ensures an increased food supply per pair, and reduces the probability of predator concentration and transmission of diseases or parasites. Territoriality may also facilitate mating, inasmuch as unmated females will be attracted to males through their territorial behavior (calls, visual displays, olfactory signals), which thus may serve both to repel other conspecific males and to attract unmated females. When rival males encroach on a territorial boundary, threat displays or fights are likely to ensure. The relative tendency of a male to attack diminishes near the boundaries of its territory and eventually results in ambivalent agonistic behavior at its extreme edge. The territorial boundaries are thus often somewhat fluid, frequently changing with day-to-day encounters. When escape tendencies overbalance those of attack, the animal may retreat or perhaps exhibit *appeasement gestures* which indicate its subordinate position and may serve to break off attack responses by the other individual. Typically, appeasement gestures represent motor patterns which are the opposite of those used in attack (for example, slimming the plumage or pelage, head turning, lowering of spines), or may even involve exposing vulnerable body areas to the dominant animal. Paradoxically, this sudden exposure to vulnerability appears to be typical of those species most able to kill one another (carnivores for example), whereas many species not having the ability of readily hurting one another have not evolved well-defined appeasement gestures and cannot so quickly break off an attack.

A special case of territoriality is found in various birds that gather at common display grounds, sometimes called *arenas* or *leks*. For example, males of various grassland species of grouse, such as sharp-tailed grouse (*Pedioecetes phasianellus*), sage grouse (*Centrocercus urophasianus*) and prairie chickens (*Tympanuchus cupido*), defend miniature territories, often of only 30 to 100 square yards, on which they respectively "dance," "strut," and "boom," and to which the females are attracted for copulation (Fig. 6). Although the males all appear to behave identically, the females are attracted only to certain dominant and centrally located birds called "master cocks." In sage grouse it has been observed that as many as 75 per cent of the females (up to twenty-one in one morning) may be fertilized by a single master cock, and one observer reported that two male prairie chickens controlling relatively large and central territories were responsible for over 70 per cent of the observed copulations. In the tropical forest-dwelling manakins (Pipridae) the brightly-colored males may perform within hearing distance but not in sight of one another ("exploded arenas"), or in true arenas, where the birds behave as sexual rivals; or they may even participate in joint ("collective") male displays, thus apparently increasing their attraction value to females.

In the same way that extensive reproductive fighting is often avoided by territorial behavior, nonreproductive fighting is frequently reduced by the establishment of *social hierarchies*, or "peck orders." Such dominance hierarchies can develop only in relatively stable social aggregations made up of members having the capacity for individual recognition. Frequently these hierarchies are developed fairly early in the life of the individual or shortly after the development of a social aggregation, often as a result of only a single encounter with each of the other members of the group. Once established, peck orders in birds tend to be fairly stable, at least during the nonreproductive periods. In species such as redpolls (*Acanthis flammeus*) the females, usually subordinate to males, seasonally assume dominance when they come into reproductive condition. It has been found that in jackdaws newly paired females assume the same rank as their mates. Although typically only a single animal (usually an adult male) stands at the top of a dominance hierarchy, in baboons (*Papio*) several of the strongest males share dominance over the other males and females, and assume the primary responsibilities of protecting the troop. In the red deer (*Cervus elaphus*) a mature female may lead the herd. Among birds the dominance hierarchy may be of a linear, or "straight-line" type, but frequently a more complex arrangement emerges, particularly in larger groups and among the midranking animals where the relationships may be unstable. Dominance hierarchies are of obvious value to social animals, particularly those lacking mutually exclusive territories during reproduction, since they allow for the advantages of group living without the problems of frequent fighting. Furthermore, by fostering reproduction of the fittest individuals, they may gradually improve the species.

Nonreproductive fighting may also be reduced by maintaining territories during nonbreeding periods, or by *mutual avoidance* when no clear dominance relationship exists. A good example is the tendency of large mammalian predators to avoid encroaching on the hunting grounds of others of their species through their recognition of and respect for territorial marker signs such as fecal piles, urinating places, barked trees, and the like.

Predator defense among animals includes a variety of behavior responses that range from strictly defensive maneuvers (fleeing, freezing, hiding) or "sham threats" (exposure of pseudo-warning signals), to actual threats or attacks (Fig. 4). The "mobbing" response of small birds to various predators provides a good example of the last category; by a concerted and noisy attack from the prey, the predator is usually unable to single out a single victim and will often abandon the hunt when the entire prey population has been alerted to its presence.

COOPERATIVE BEHAVIOR

Concerted mobbing responses by birds, or the defensive "ring" formation assumed by musk oxen (*Ovibos moschatus*), are examples of *cooperative behavior* by which the survival of the social unit is perpetuated, sometimes at the expense of some individuals. Intraspecific cooperation occurs in relatively few groups of animals; in the insects it is typical of the truly social forms (ants, termites, and social bees and wasps), and among vertebrates it is found in a few groups of gregarious mammals (primates, ungulates, a few carnivores, and some rodents).

In general there is a relationship between sociality and herbivorous food habits, since herbivores have reduced intraspecific foraging competition and are of lessened danger to one another. The carnivorous but gregarious dog family Canidae provides an exception; here hunting is done in a cooperative manner, with the pack joining in the spoils.

The highest form of instinctive cooperative behavior is found in the social insects which have a subdivision of labor resulting in a *caste system*. In such rigid organizations different individuals may be both morphologically and behaviorally differentiated to perform only a certain part of the colonies' activities, and thus "soldiers," "workers," "queens," and (in termites) "kings" may be recognized. This caste differentiation may be in part genetically controlled (according to the sex of the individual), but is also partly regulated by such environmental aspects as kind and amount of food consumed in larval stages (distinguishing worker from queen bees) or the presence of "social hormones" (pheromones), which may control caste differentiation in termite colonies. In the social insects the usual manner by which colonies develop is one of growth or differentiation, often beginning with a single fertilized female, the future queen, or by a small nucleus of reproductive individuals that is reinforced by succeeding generations.

In contrast to the differentiation of insect colonies, many vertebrate social groups develop through a process of fusion or "condensation," resulting from the mutual attraction of unrelated individuals into larger social units. Furthermore, these social groups may be transitory in nature and frequently develop during nonbreeding seasons when sexual and territorial tendencies wane. Permanent, closed social systems do occur in a few mammals having a complex home that is built and maintained by a monogamous family group (beavers), or where there is need for an elaborate antipredator warning system throughout a community of polygamous family groups (prairie dogs). In both situations cooperative behavior reaches a high degree of development, and a *communication system* is an important means of social integration. The primates provide another example of relatively permanent and variably closed social systems in which protection from predators is achieved by effective auditory communication systems.

Primates also well illustrate, through their mutual grooming activities, a final category of cooperative behavior sometimes designated as *mutual care*. There can be little doubt that some primates will also attempt to aid disabled or endangered members of their troop in emergencies, and the same observation has been made for elephants and dolphins.

REPRODUCTIVE BEHAVIOR

A large category of social behavior is that associated with sex and reproduction. The basic function of reproductive behavior is fertilization and continuity of the species, and in many invertebrates this purpose is achieved with few or no behavioral correlates. External, random fertilization of gametes is typical of many marine and fresh water invertebrates, and may be triggered by various external stimuli such as water temperature, tidal rhythms, or other factors. *Epidemic spawning* may also be achieved by the release of pheromones stimulating gamete emission in other individuals. Many marine polychaete annelids such as the Bermuda fireworm achieve simultaneous *individual spawning* by delaying their gamete emission until individuals of opposite sexes are attracted to one another in the water, in this case by luminous signals. Such increased efficiency in reproduction points the way to more complex behavior associated with fertilization. The evolution of *internal fertilization* through passage of sperm packets or copulation was another important landmark in achieving individual reproductive efficiency. However, actual pair-formation, in which a persistent behavioral bond between reproductive individuals is established and consists of something more than sexual association during the time of fertilization, is limited to the vertebrates, especially birds, some mammals, and a few fish.

In birds the general cycle of sexual activity in temperate zone species is usually dependent upon variations in photoperiod, with the increasing hours of daylight during spring serving to stimulate the anterior pituitary to produce gonadotrophic hormones. Although this stimulus may be adequate to bring a male into reproductive condition, females often require the presence of a sexually active male to bring them into readiness for laying. But in pigeons, the sound of males in adjacent cages may provide enough aural stimulation for females to undergo ovulation, and even the visual stimulation provided by a mirror has proven adequate. Fraser Darling has emphasized the importance of these general visual and auditory stimuli in facilitating the synchronized breeding of colonial birds (the so-called *Darling effect*), and in such species it appears that large colonies are often more successful than small ones.

Together with the increase in sexual responses produced by pair-forming behavior, there may be a correlated reduction in hostile tendencies toward the mate. In territorial songbirds that show no sexual dimorphism, as in the North American thrushes studied by William Dilger, initial responses of the male to females appearing on its territory may be strictly hostile as it would respond toward a rival male. An unmated female will avoid provoking attacks by the male, and if she remains on the territory the male may gradually come to accept her presence and ultimately respond sexually toward her. In herring gulls and other birds the female performs infantile responses such as begging, thus eliciting nonhostile responses from the male.

The importance of sexual behavior as an isolating mechanism cannot be overemphasized, but a discussion of it will be reserved for Chapter 12. It need only be said here that the isolating factors may depend upon the responses of either or both sexes, and of course must be most effective in those species which are closely related and for which other sources of isolating mechanisms are inadequate.

Among species having a distinct separation between the time of initial sexual encounters and that of gamete release it is often convenient to distinguish between pair-forming (sometimes called *gamosematic*) and fertilization behavior. There are several advantages to an individual sexual association, or pair bond, which may be established sometime prior to fertilization and may persist through the reproductive cycle. Such a bond would provide a more efficient potential isolating mechanism through the possible "correction" of incipient mistakes prior to fertilization, a greater efficiency of fertilization as a result of prolonged sexual contact through the reproductive cycle, and the possibility of the male protecting the female and/or young during this vulnerable period. Strictly *monogamous* pair bonds are not common, although they do occur in most birds having altricial young, as well as in various carnivorous terrestrial mammals that have relatively altricial offspring. In birds these bonds usually persist only for one brood or for a single breeding season. Monogamous pair bonds may persist through more than one season in such sea birds as petrels, which have a remarkable fidelity to a particular nest site, thus facilitating the reestablishment of earlier pair bonds. It is generally believed that a few birds including geese and swans may pair for life, and it is known that at least some penguins and various other relatively long-lived birds such as gulls have sustained pair bonds lasting several years. Among mammals, wolves are said to have monogamous pair bonds which persist more than one season, and beavers and gibbons are reported to have monogamous and potentially permanent bonds. Most monogamous animals show relatively little sexual dimorphism, and in birds, at least, both sexes commonly perform very similar displays. Such *mutual displays* include the "penguin dance" of grebes, similar "dances" of albatrosses, and various swan, goose, and penguin displays (Fig. 3). However, minor sexual differences are usually present in such mutual displays, and may be important in preventing homosexual pairing. Many species which exhibit sexually dimorphic pair-forming displays have simpler and frequently mutual displays that function as *pair-maintaining* mechanisms. In ducks these have been called "prenuptial" and "nuptial" displays, respectively.

In monogamous bird species it is usually possible to recognize special ritualized behavior patterns associated with fertilization. These include *precopulatory displays, copulatory displays,* and *postcopulatory displays.* Precopulatory displays are often similar in the two sexes (*mutual*), but may be performed by the male alone (*solo*) before or after the female exhibits a disposition for copulation. Such precopulatory displays probably serve to reduce nonsexual tendencies during copulation, and may also provide a final source of behavioral isolation between species. During copulation there may be calling on the part of one or both sexes, quivering or shaking movements of the wings by the male, or other stereotyped behavior that might also tend to ensure the effectiveness of the mating. Frequently birds exhibit postcopulatory displays which may be performed mutually or by only one sex. The function of such displays which occur too late to function as isolating mechanisms is still dubious, but they may serve to maintain pair bonds or to prevent hostile responses. It is not uncommon among waterfowl for a female to attack a male following an unsuccessful copulation after which no postcopulatory displays were performed, thus the value of ritualized postcopulatory behavior in inhibiting such hostile responses should not be overlooked.

Polygamy (here including bigamy) is relatively common in at least some groups of birds and mammals, and can occur either in the form of *polygyny* (two or more females per male) or *polyandry* (two or more males per female). In birds, polygyny occurs in several groups having precocial young, including some of the large ratites, many galliformes (such as the typical pheasants) and others. Among passerines having altricial young, polygyny has been found in certain blackbirds (*Agelaius*) and wrens (*Troglodytes*). It may occur either in the form of contemporaneous polygyny ("harem formation"), as in pheasants, or as successive

Fig. 3. Mutual Displays of Gannet (A), Adelie Penguin (B), Wandering Albatross (C), and Four Species of Grebes (D-G).

polygyny. It has been suggested that among passerines polygyny is fostered by an unbalanced adult sex ratio in favor of females, or the presence of relatively productive feeding areas but restricted nesting sites. The presence of abundant food would make it likely that a female could rear the altricial young without assistance from the male. Among mammals, polygyny occurs in such aquatic carnivores as sea lions and seals, and also in most large ungulates except rhinos and swine. In the case of the ungulates the young are relatively precocial, often being able to run about within a day or so after birth, and the marine carnivores have a relatively unlimited food supply and no dangers from other predators.

In both birds and mammals there is a direct correlation between the presence of polygyny and relative degree of sexual dimorphism; thus, males which collect "harems" usually are larger, more conspicuous or colorful, and better equipped with weapons of attack or defense than are those of monogamous species. Both sexes may display during pair formation, but the female is usually behaviorally "submissive" or "inferior," and generally the sexual displays are markedly different in the two sexes. The conspicuous male displays which attract females in polygynous or promiscuous species are probably better referred to as *advertisement* displays than pair-forming displays.

Polyandry is found in a number of birds but probably no mammals, the viviparity of mammals presumably making this an inefficient mode of reproduction. In such birds as phalaropes (Phalaropodidae) the females are brighter than the males, do the active courting, and defend the territory. After laying the eggs, the female is freed to locate another male and produce another clutch of eggs, an obvious reproductive advantage to the species. Although most of the birds which practice polyandry have precocial young, a few cases of polyandry among birds having altricial young have been reported. The superb blue wren (*Malurus cyaneus*) of Australia has recently been reported to be apparently polyandrous. In this species, however, the male is brightly colored during the breeding season whereas the female is protectively patterned. It has been suggested that there is an unbalanced sex ratio in favor of males and that the assistance of "supernumerary males" in caring for nearly fledged but dependent young may allow the species to rear the maximum number of broods in a favorable season.

Complete promiscuity is typical of a few groups of birds, and is relatively common in mammals. The rodents, insectivores, and bats, in particular, are generally promiscuous. Among birds, promiscuity is especially typical of certain families, including various birds of paradise and bower birds, several grouse species, many hummingbirds, and the manakins. In all these avian groups, there is, to varying degrees, a tendency toward elaborate male displays and/or colorful plumage patterns resulting from the combined effects of sexual selection and the importance of correct species recognition at the time of copulation, in the absence of a preceding pair bond. Among the bower birds there is an interesting inverse relationship between the degree of male coloration and the complexity of the bower built by the male; in this case the species-recognition characteristics have been "transferred" to an inanimate object that the female is attracted to and where copulation occurs. In decorating their bowers, males of some species tend to select objects colored in a manner similar to themselves; thus, the male satin bower bird (*Ptilonorhynchus violaceus*) selectively chooses blue objects for its bower, and even "paints" it with the juice of blue berries, spread with a brush of plant material.

Sexual selection is a less promising explanation for sexual dimorphism in such animals as fish and insects, particularly the latter. Yet, it has been found that a female jewel fish (*Hemichromis bimaculatus*) will select the most highly colored of several possible mates, and sexual dimorphism is quite common in this family (Cichlidae) of oviparous fishes. Among some fish having internal fertilization, considerable sexual dimorphism also occurs, as in various species of the family Characidae. In this group the male's dimorphism and intensity of sexual display appear to be related to its success in fertilizing the relatively passive females. The cumulative effect of the male's displays in facilitating copulation may thus be regarded as a source of sexual selection. G. Kingsley Noble has suggested that several other factors may also favor the development of sexual dimorphism in fishes. These include its possible functions in male territorial behavior, in sex or species recognition, or in parental recognition among those species exhibiting parental behavior. Bright male coloration is especially typical of territorial fish in which the male guards the nest or young. In the Cichlidae both sexes are usually colorful among monogamous species in which both sexes care for the young. In some fish, such as certain catfish, there may be territorial defense and parental care but no bright coloration; however, vision in these species is apparently subordinate to olfactory or other cues.

Unlike birds, fish are often able to change their color patterns and brightness to fit their internal state. Color variation is shown particularly well in the cichlid *Tilapia mossambica,* on the basis of which it is possible to estimate the fish's "tendencies" and its probable ensuing behavior patterns. The fish is thus able to change from a conspicuous sexual coloration to an inconspicuous concealing pattern when predators are near. The change in color is evidently regulated by the autonomic nervous system, particularly adrenalin and acetylcholine, and this explains why the patterns are such an accurate manifestation of the animal's internal state.

PARENTAL BEHAVIOR

Following copulation or spawning, the fate of the fertilized eggs or nearly born young may largely depend on subsequent attention by one or both parents. Apart from the social insects, parental care is an uncommon situation in invertebrates. Egg-brooding or carrying of the eggs or young occurs in some cephalopod mollusks and in certain arthropods, such as the females of various spiders, crustaceans, isopods, millepeds, and scorpions. Among vertebrates, parental care is typical of mammals, birds, some reptiles, some amphibians, and various fish. In the "mouth-breeding" species of Cichlidae the male or female carries the developing eggs or newly hatched young in its mouth, and in some species of catfish the male does the same thing. In other fish the embryos develop in special brooding pouches, as for example in male sea horses *(Hippocampus).* A similar situation prevails in certain toads, such as the Surinam toad *(Pipa pipa),* the young of which develop on the female's back, and in other species are carried in the vocal pouch of the male. Nest-building is performed by some fish, such as the sticklebacks and the "bubble-nest" builders (Anabantidae). In a number of South American and Asian tree frogs the nest of various species may be a simple mud enclosure by the edge of a pond, a mass of foam produced by beating the eggs with the feet, or may even be located in the leaves of trees closely overhanging the water. An actual defense of the nest is found in certain species.

Among birds, numerous complex behavior patterns associated with the care of eggs and young have evolved. Among these the following categories might be mentioned: nest-building behavior, mate-recognition and nest-relief displays, incubation behavior, and parental care of the young. True nests utilized for breeding purposes are also constructed by some mammals, such as harvest mice, some squirrels, wood rats, beavers, and muskrats. A prolonged period of caring for the young is typical of both mammals and birds, and a few other vertebrates. The male bowfin (*Amia*) may remain with and guard the young the entire first summer following hatching, and a female alligator may remain with her young for a period of from one to three years. In both, the adults guard the nest or young with great fervor, and the bowfin may use diversionary tactics when other animals approach the nest.

After birth or hatching, the young often interact behaviorally with the parents in a manner that favors their survival. Gaping responses of altricial birds, which serve as a stimulus for parental feeding and are performed in an intensity directly related to the degree of hunger, serve as a useful regulator of feeding rate. Conspicuous gape markings, papillae, or color patterns are commonly exhibited by such young birds, particularly in species which do not nest in completely exposed situations where these markings might attract predators. Remarkably, the gape patterns of some brood parasitic birds, the widow birds (*Vidua*) of Africa, closely mimic those markings of the host species' young, just as individual female European cuckoos lay eggs with color patterns closely resembling those of the particular host species.

In many birds, particularly ground-nesting species, one or both parents may respond to possible predators near the nest or young by performing *distraction displays,* sometimes called "broken-wing acts" or "rodent runs," which no doubt tend to lure the intruding animal away from the brood. The evolutionary origin of such displays, which may expose conspicuous tail or wing patterns, remains speculative, but perhaps the best theory is that they are derived from ambivalent compromise movements reflecting the parents' conflicting tendencies to flee from and remain with the young or eggs. The selective advantage of such diversionary behavior is obvious, and the gradual improvement of these motor patterns to closely resemble those of a disabled bird might be expected to occur.

In avian species where both sexes care for the young, and multiple broods are typical, one parent will sometimes look after the first brood while the other incubates (European nightjar), or the pair may take turns at the various duties (ringed plover). The common gallinule (*Gallinula chloropus*) is even more remarkable; the young of the first brood commonly help feed their younger siblings! Among mammals, the female alone generally cares for the young, but in such carnivores as wolves, foxes, and weasels the male may provide the dependent family with much of its food. In some ungulates the male may actively protect the young, and in a few, such as giraffes, large "nurseries" (or crèches) or weaned young may be formed. The same is true of certain penguins, flamingos, and ducks.

The immature offspring of birds and mammals may remain associated with one or both parents for some time, often until they become reproductively mature or until the parents again come into breeding condition. During this time a certain amount of information may be transmitted between the generations, such as hunting techniques in the case of predators or the acquisition of migratory "traditions" as in many waterfowl. The importance and efficiency of such information transmission doubtless varies greatly among different species, but in any case is largely dependent upon an effective communication system. The methods and functions of animal communication will be considered next.

SUGGESTED READING

ALLEE, W. C., *The Social Life of Animals*. New York: W. W. Norton & Company, Inc., 1938, 293 pp. (Also available in paperback edition from Beacon Press, Boston.)

ARMSTRONG, E. A., *Bird Display and Behaviour*. London: Lindsay Drummond, Ltd., 1947, 431 pp. (Also available in paperback edition from Dover Publications, Inc., New York.)

BEACH, F. A. (ed.), *Sex and Behavior*. New York: John Wiley & Sons, Inc., 1965, 592 pp.

DARLING, F. F., *A Herd of Red Deer*. London: Oxford University Press, 1937, 215 pp. (Also available in paperback edition from Doubleday & Company, Inc., New York.)

EIBL-EIBESFELDT, IRENÄUS, "The Fighting Behavior of Animals," *Scientific American*, December, 1961, pp. 112-122. (Available in offprint form.)

ETKIN, W. (ed.), *Social Behavior and Organization Among Vertebrates*, Chicago: University of Chicago Press, 1964, 307 pp.

LEHRMAN, D. S., "The Reproductive Behavior of Ring Doves." *Scientific American*, November, 1964, pp. 48-54. (Available in offprint form.)

LINDAUER, M., "Social Behavior and Mutual Communication," In ROCKSTEIN, MORRIS, (ed.), *The Physiology of Insecta*. New York: Academic Press, 1965, Vol. II, pp. 124-167.

MICHENER, C. D., and MICHENER, M. H., *American Social Insects*. New York: D. Van Nostrand Company, Inc., 1951, 267 pp.

THOMPSON, W. R., "Social Behavior." In ROE, A., and SIMPSON, G. G. (eds.), *Behavior and Evolution*. New Haven, Conn.: Yale University Press, 1958, 557 pp.

TINBERGEN, N., *Social Behaviour in Animals*. New York: John Wiley & Sons, Inc., 1953, 150 pp.

WHEELER, W. N., *The Social Insects: Their Origin and Evolution*. New York: Harcourt Brace and Company, 1928, 359 pp.

CHAPTER 7

Communication

Although the human species is preeminent in its capacity for the transmission of concrete and abstract information between individuals, it is also possible to observe a variety of analogous behavior patterns in nonhumans that range all the way from nondirected general information transfer to the interchange of highly specific quantitative and qualitative information between individuals. Thus, it is difficult to define adequately animal communication, but a broad interpretation that includes essentially all types of information transfer within and between species would seem desirable. At its lowest level we might consider that essentially reflex-like responses toward certain stimuli (pain, distress, food) to which other individuals are sensitive and become alerted represent a kind of inadvertent communication system. When such simple or more complex responses are dependent upon the presence of other individuals and are clearly directed toward them, the recognition of an adaptively functional communication system is necessary. The highest level of communication is reached when the responses of the "receiver" individual are effective in modifying the kind or amount of information sent by the "transmitter" individual, and a definite two-way information transfer system is achieved.

CATEGORIES AND FUNCTIONS OF COMMUNICATION

Animal signals, whether reflex-like or "purposive," can be broadly grouped into two somewhat overlapping categories, depending on whether they are transmitted primarily within species or between species. *Intraspecific* signal systems include a variety of signals primarily directed toward specific individuals, as well as various social signals more generally directed toward others of the same species.

Predominantly *interspecific* signals include a spectrum of attack- and escape-related responses that are often difficult to interpret correctly. Thus, *warning signals* imply a definite threat that is directed toward another animal of the same or different species. Similar *intimidating signals* may be produced under the same conditions by species unable to follow up their threat effectively. These merge with *pseudo-warning signals* of innocuous species that behaviorally mimic other species less likely to be attacked for various reasons (Figs. 1 and 4). Finally, there are signals such as distraction displays which serve to *decoy* an intruder from some location. *Alarm* calls of prey species, although directed to conspecific social members, may be recognized and responded to by other prey species, particularly if similar alarm signals are employed by both. Many songbird species have very similar alarm notes distinguishing ground as well as aerial predators, and thus are able to understand and mutually benefit from this common link in their communication systems.

Several major functions of signaling behavior, apart from the categories already mentioned, doubtless exist. One important function is *species and sex recognition,* allowing for social integration and efficient reproduction within each species. As a result, there is frequently a species-specificity of these signals, both as regards the signaling structures utilized and the signaling behavior employed. Within the broad framework of species recognition there may also be more specific *individual recognition* of mates or members of a social group on the basis of minor variations in signaling behavior. Frequently, signaling behavior provides an external indication of the animal's *internal state.* Probably two opposing factors are involved here. The first favors uniform performance of the signaling behavior, thus increasing certainty of effective transmission. This effectiveness might be achieved by a stereotyped, all-or-none mechanism that indicates a general range of internal states and results in a uniform performance, or "typical intensity," of response each time the signal is given. Typical intensity responses are presumed to evolve through a gradual ritualization and increased stereotypy of postures, movements, or sounds which previously may have had no direct signal value. On the other hand, it is a common phenomenon to find continually graded responses which range from one extreme to another, and these may provide a very accurate

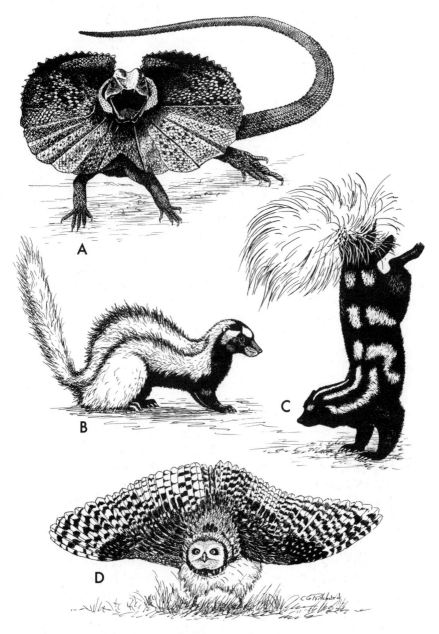

Fig. 4. Warning and Intimidation Displays of Frilled Lizard (A), Zorille (B), Spotted Skunk (C), and Short-eared Owl (D).

reflection of the animal's internal state. For example, the facial expressions of humans and other primates show such graded stages, as does the degree of feather or pelage erection of birds and mammals in various agonistic situations.

One last major function of signaling behavior is in promoting *social integration,* such as group coordination or concerted antipredator responses. Thus, signals may announce the location of the signaling individual, a predator, a nest site, a territory, or a food supply. It may also serve to maintain social units through contact calls or assembly calls, or may provide guidance signals to others in the social unit. Even interspecific guidance signals are known; the famous honey-guides (*Indicator*) of Africa are such an example. These birds actually guide various species of mammals to bee nests, and are able to digest the wax left by such animals after they have broken open the comb in search of honey.

Any signal system must, of course, fall within the sensory and motor ranges of the species concerned and must be ecologically appropriate. An efficient signal system should have several of the following features: qualitative or quantitative specificity, rapid rate of information dissemination, efficiency over considerable distances, directionality of transmission, and a wide range of information content. Other possibly important features may be a persistence of the signal or, contrariwise, the ability to start and stop it quickly. A remarkable variety of signaling devices have evolved that fill these criteria to varying degrees. These devices include visual, chemical, acoustic, tactile, and electrical methods of communication. Of these, the most information is available concerning visual and auditory signals, since humans are most able to recognize and evaluate these. Birds have sensory abilities similar to man's, and therefore many of the best-studied examples of visual and auditory communications stem from this source. Some other nonhuman mammals, especially diurnal forms such as large ungulates, utilize visual signals extensively too, but most mammals probably rely heavily on olfactory signaling devices.

VISUAL COMMUNICATION

Visual signaling devices occur widely in birds, diurnal mammals, fishes, reptiles, and also are present in some poisonous amphibians, which employ warning coloration. Many invertebrates, especially those with large eyes and diurnal activity patterns, also use visual devices. Luminous signaling devices are utilized by various marine invertebrates, various deep-water fish, and some nocturnal insects. The origins of visual signaling devices are probably diverse but appear to be of three general types. Effects of the autonomic nervous system, such as hair or feather erection, flushing of the skin, or blood engorgement of wattles and combs, are doubtless of great significance and clearly account for the origin of many visual displays. Closely related to these are movements or postures that provide a clue to the animal's future behavior. These preliminary, or "intention," movements might include such activities as the preflight head movements of birds, the crouching of a carnivore about to spring forward, or wing-spreading by an insect about to fly.

Ambivalent or irrelevant movements which occur during conflict situations are believed to provide a third important source of origin for visual displays. These seemingly functionless activities may gradually become ritualized and incorporated into social displays. The frequency with which postures derived from "comfort" movements (such as stretching, preening, bathing, shaking, and grooming) and certain maintenance activities (such as drinking, eating, or eliminative behavior) have been ritualized suggest that such so-called "displacement" activities are indeed important sources of visual signals. Additionally, redirected motor patterns may also become ritualized into visual displays, as may the postures or movements resulting from the simultaneous or alternate activation of relatively opposing motor patterns. The "gesture of repulsion" performed by many female ducks when approached by a strange male is a good example, since it simultaneously combines elements of escape (retracted head, retreating movements) and attack (opened bill, fluffed feathers). The "inciting" display of female ducks is clearly a variably ritualized result of the alteration of motor patterns involved in attack (toward a strange drake) and escape (toward a mate or potential mate).

Some of the most famous visual signaling devices are those employed by honeybees for guidance purposes. Although these have been most thoroughly studied in the common honeybee (*Apis mellifera*), they are also known to occur in the other three species of *Apis*. All four species have a means of communicating information concerning the distance and direction of food sources, but they differ in certain respects. Only three of the four species are able to convert their signaling behavior that provides directional information from a horizontal surface (direct sun orientation) to a vertical surface (gravity orientation). The species (*A. florea*) that "dances" only on horizontal surfaces does so on the upper surface of its relatively flat-topped comb, whereas the other species typically dance on vertical comb surfaces. The quantitative means by which distance information is transmitted also differs among the species. In the "waggle dance" there is a close correlation between the speed of the dance and the distance to the food source. When the food source is at a common distance, the four species show different average speeds of dancing. Moreover, the species differ as to the minimal distance at which they transfer from the "round dance," which does not impart direction information, to the more informative waggle dance. Even within various races of the common honeybee it has been found that local "dialects" exist, in which these same kinds of quantitative variations occur.

The evolution of such a complex and nearly unbelievable communication system as found in the honeybees must have been an extremely long and slow process, which in its early stages must have been barely efficient enough to be of selective advantage. However, by studying the related stingless bees (Meliponi) of the tropics, some indications of how this process may have developed are emerging. Eleven species of these social bees have been studied and all have been found to have some means of alerting the colony to a food source. However, the efficiency of their communication systems vary greatly. In one species (*Trigona iridipennis*) a worker that has found a food source simply flies back to the comb and excitedly runs about, alerting the other workers of the existence but not the location of food. However, in *Trigona postica*, the worker bee returns to the colony only after making a series of trail marks at short intervals on the substrate. This marking is done by rubbing the mandibles on convenient objects such as leaves, and the secretions of a special mandibular gland provides a chemical guideline for other workers to follow. This type of communication system is of special advantage to these forest-dwelling species, in which vertical movements may be as important as horizontal movements, and a single-coordinate directional system may thus be inadequate.

Visual signals, then, have the advantages of qualitative and quantitative specificity, a very rapid rate of dissemination, and conspicuousness in daylight, but they are of no value at night unless they are luminous. The signals can be readily started and stopped, and may have a wide information content, especially in animals with color vision. It is no surprise, therefore, that the most colorful animals (those having colored signaling devices) are also those with color vision, such as most insects, fish, and birds, but relatively few mammals.

ACOUSTICAL COMMUNICATION

Acoustical signaling devices have the advantage of being invisible, since permanently colorful but vulnerable animals may "pay" for their visual signals by rendering themselves more conspicuous to predators. Sounds also penetrate well in both air and water, regardless of light conditions or turbidity, and have a high potential for specificity and information range. The degree of directionality and the ability of the receiver to "home in" on the signal probably vary, and the latter depends on the binaural reception capabilities of the species. Acoustic signaling behavior is widespread in mammals, birds, anuran amphibians, and some groups of insects. Among aquatic animals it is well developed in cetaceans, some fish, and a few crustaceans. Perhaps the most complex vocalizations are to be found among birds and higher primates, particularly man. The howler monkey (*Alouatta*) has a vocabulary of some fifteen to twenty vocalizations, and in captivity chimpanzees (*Pan*) have been found to utter over thirty different sounds. Other highly vocal mammals are the dolphins and whales, and some gregarious rodents are also moderately vocal. At least some of the marine mammals utilize sounds as a basis for sonar navigation, and similarly ultrasonic sounds are employed by the smaller bats for nocturnal navigation and prey-catching.

Auditory signaling behavior has been particularly well studied in birds, partly because of its conspicuousness and also because the frequencies of sounds utilized largely correspond to the sensory range of humans. As stated earlier, many birds have numerous call notes of relatively simple acoustical structure which convey important types of information. Among numerous songbirds studied it has been found that there are usually between ten and twenty distinct call notes (but up to twenty-five reported) and from one to five song types, producing a total usual "vocabulary" of fifteen to twenty-five or more vocal signals. This number compares favorably with the vocabularies of wild primates and emphasizes the significance of sound to most birds. In some nocturnal birds, including the South American oilbird (*Steatornis*) and the Asian swiftlets (*Collocalia*), it has also been proven that a sonar navigational system exists.

Vocalizations are especially important to birds that cannot readily utilize visual signals, such as those species ·inhabiting dense vegetation, or where bright coloration would render a species vulnerable to predation. There is, therefore, a direct correlation between the presence of elaborate or loud songs and the density of typical habitat, and to some degree an inverse correlation between bright coloration and vocal abilities. The combination of conspicuous coloration and elaborate vocalizations is usually limited to those species that for some reason have reduced dangers of predation, or for which the effectiveness of sexual selection overbalances that of antipredator adaptations.

Because of the almost unlimited potential for interspecies variability in songs, such as differences in pitch, volume, and quality, it is not surprising that vocalizations may provide important bases for the maintenance of reproductive isolation between closely related species. Vocalizations appear to be especially significant in certain families such as the tyrant flycatchers (Tyrannidae), in which a large number of fairly closely related species may breed in the same area and which often lack marked visual differences. It has been suggested that the alder flycatcher (*Empidonax traillii*) actually consists of two morphologically almost identical *sibling species*, which differ primarily in their song patterns. Probably, innate differences in the calls of the eastern and western meadowlarks (*Sturnella*) combine with minor ecological differences to maintain reproductive isolation between these closely similar species.

Unlike the laryngeal voice production of mammals, birds utilize the syrinx for their vocalizations. Some mammals and birds also produce certain nonvocal sounds such as tail-slapping by beavers (*Castor*) or vibration sounds of special wing and tail feathers by birds. However, mechanically produced sounds are probably not so important in vertebrates as they are in invertebrates. Great interspecies variation of anatomical structure exists in the syrinx of birds; moreover, sexual dimorphism in syringeal and tracheal structure is not uncommon. In males of many duck species the presence of a bony syringeal *bulla* serves to produce sexual dimorphism in vocalizations and also results in species-specificity of sound production. Inflation and deflation of nonsyringeal structures such as tracheal air sacs or the esophagus often serves as a supplementary source of vocal or visual signals, as for example in the displays of various grouse that noisily inflate the esophagus and simultaneously expose colorful and unfeathered skin areas (Fig. 6).

Among the reptiles only the crocodilia are very vocal, but hissing or grunting sounds are made by various snakes and turtles, and mechanical stridulation sounds produced by friction or vibration also occur. On the other hand, many of the amphibians use vocal sounds extensively for signaling purposes. The frogs and toads are especially good examples of the importance of acoustical signaling. These species often possess special air sacs which serve as resonators of the laryngeal sounds produced, and some species exhibit several types of calls. Nonreproductive calls include warning and distress calls, and calls uttered during the reproductive period include those that serve for territorial announcement, attraction of females, and possibly other purposes. It has been amply proven that frogs and toads utilize male calls as reproductive isolating mechanisms, and there is also evidence that females will be attracted to those conspecific males that are most vocal, suggesting that sexual selection may also be a factor promoting the evolution of anuran vocal signals.

Acoustic behavior is conspicuous in certain groups of insects, particularly certain Orthoptera and Homoptera. Sound production by the social bees and ants is inconspicuous and has been little studied, but may be of considerable social significance. The functions of insect sounds are evidently numerous. Perhaps the most common function is the facilitation of mating, with the attraction calls of one sex (usually the male) serving to bring the sexes together. Alternate calling by both sexes for the same purpose occurs in a few groups. A function related to mating is that of achieving reproductive isolation, which has been demonstrated conclusively for certain Orthoptera. A territorial dispersion function has been suggested for crickets and "cracker-locusts" (*Cercotet-tix*). There is little doubt that the opposite effect occurs, that of facilitating social groupings of reproductive individuals, as exemplified by the aggregations of cicadas. Several probable warning or intimidation sounds are produced by insects, such as the droning of wasps, the sounds made by certain lepidoteran pupae when disturbed, or the remarkable chemical "explosion" produced by the bombardier beetle (*Brachinus*). Social integration signals are also known, including the departing signals of grasshoppers and the "disturbance sounds" of cicadas (which cause other individuals to stop calling). Finally, special guidance signals are known to occur in insects. It has recently been determined that during the straight run of the worker honeybee's waggle dance a sound is produced that is proportional in length to the distance of the food source. This sound apparently provides alternative or additional distance information to that indicated by the speed of the dance. The scout bee evidently estimates this distance according to its flight time back to the hive, by flying at a constant ground speed. It is also known that the queen bees vocally communicate with the workers through various sounds, the functions of which are still unclear.

CHEMICAL COMMUNICATION

Chemical signaling behavior is almost certainly as important as the other methods, but unfortunately little is known about it. We can be confident that among most mammals and at least certain insects (especially Lepidoptera and Diptera) it must hold special significance for sexual attraction, reproductive isolation, and other functions such as guidance and alarm signals in colonial insects. Virgin moths of at least eleven families, after emergence from the pupae, produce remarkably effective olfactory stimuli that may attract males from great distances. The sensitivity of insects to odors has been utilized by plants in the evolution of pollination mechanisms that may be relatively specific to particular insects. The classic case of the yucca plant and its associated *Pronuba* moth might be mentioned as an example, and many fly-pollinated flowers emit fetid odors reminiscent of rotting meat.

Among vertebrates, various fish release specific "fright substances" when attacked, causing others to avoid the area. Special scent glands occur in such reptiles as the crocodilians, as well as some turtles and snakes. A few birds also produce musky odors which are still of uncertain function. However, in mammals the importance of olfactory signals cannot be denied, and a wide variety of localized scent glands exist. These are often located near the feet or genitals, where they can be readily transmitted to objects in the environment and may serve to mark territories, attract females, or both. The use of feces and urine for the marking of home ranges or territories is also prevalent in mammals. Perhaps the ultimate in olfactory signaling is the discharge of highly disagreeable secretions from special scent glands as a defensive maneuver. This occurs in a number of species of skunks (Mustelidae), which frequently exhibit warning coloration in the form of black and white stripes or spots. In their similarities of pelage patterns, threat behavior, and the vileness of their scents, the African weasel-like zorille (*Poecilictis*) and American skunks (*Mephitis* and *Spilogale*) exhibit a remarkable degree of parallel evolution (Fig. 4).

To illustrate the importance of olfactory stimuli in mammalian reproductive patterns, it has been found that when a recently fertilized female mouse is exposed to the odors of a strange male, her hormonal balance is sufficiently affected as to inhibit pregnancy ("Bruce effect"). Likewise, the odors of male mice are able to influence the estrus cycles of females ("Whitten effect"), even when physical contact between them is prevented. These examples point out one of the unique facets of olfactory signaling devices that are not found in the other methods of communication, the persistence of the signal. Such persistence means that territories can be easily marked out and proclaimed in absentia. It seems possible, however, that these odors might also attract predators, and thus are probably primarily used by species that are relatively safe from predation.

OTHER COMMUNICATION SYSTEMS

Tactile signaling devices, unlike those previously dealt with, require physical contact between individuals or, at most, are generally effective over relatively short ranges. Vibratory or quivering movements are utilized by fish and amphibians for direct bodily stimulation or indirect stimulation via pressure receptors in the skin, such as the lateral line system. Direct tactile stimulation is likewise of great significance in the courtship of snakes. The relative rugosity or smoothness of the skin of frogs and toads may serve as an isolating mechanism during clasping, and similar tactile stimuli associated with insemination among internally fertilized species could be of important behavioral significance. The laying down of slime trails or silk lines which can be followed by other animals might be legitimately included under tactile signals, even though the behavior may not have been specifically evolved for that purpose. Males of various web-spinning spiders announce their presence at the web of a female by vibrating the web; the response of the female to this tactile stimulus will greatly affect the male's ensuing behavior.

Only recently has the importance of electrical communication systems been recognized and at least partially appreciated. Although the use of electricity by various fish for stunning or killing their prey has been widely known, and its origin speculated over, it is now known that representatives of three or four families of fish (especially the Mormyridae) may utilize relatively weak electrical signals for purposes other than defense. Thus, *Gymnarchus* has been proven to employ an electrical sonar system for detecting other objects, including other individuals of the species. In a related genus, *Gnathomaemus*, a territorial function has been proposed for the electrical signals. It is definitely known that specifically distinct discharge patterns do exist and could readily serve as a basis of social integration. It is probable that this was the original function of electricity production in these fishes, and that navigational adaptations and the use of electricity for defensive or aggressive purposes are derived functions. This explanation would help account for the evolution and adaptive value of electrical signals which are too weak to be used for defense. The use of electricity for such communication purposes demands not only electricity-producing organs (basically specialized motor end plates and muscles) but also electroreceptors. These are now known to occur in these groups of fishes, and have been proven to be highly sensitive to the detection of electric currents.

SUGGESTED READING

ALEXANDER, R. D., "The Evolution of Cricket Chirps." *Natural History,* November, 1966, pp. 27-31.

ARMSTRONG, E. A., *A Study of Bird Song.* London: Oxford University Press, 1963, 335 pp.

BUSNEL, R. G. (ed.), *Acoustic Behavior of Animals.* New York: American Elsevier Publishing Company, Inc., 1963, 933 pp.

FRINGS, H., and FRINGS, MABLE, *Animal Communication.* New York: Blaisdell Publishing Company, 1964, 204 pp.

FRISCH, K. VON, "Dialects in the Language of Bees." *Scientific American,* August, 1962, pp. 78-87. (Available in offprint form.)

HASKELL, P. T., *Insect Sounds.* Chicago: Quadrangle Books, Inc., 1961, 189 pp.

LANYON, W. E., and TAVOLGA, W. N. (eds.), *Animal Sounds and Communication.* Publication No. 7, American Institute of Biological Science. Washington, D. C.: American Institute of Biological Science, 1960, 443 pp.

LINDAUER, H., *Communication Among Social Bees.* Cambridge, Mass.: Harvard University Press, 1961, 143 pp.

LISSMAN, H. W., "Electric Location by Fishes." *Scientific American,* March, 1963, pp. 50-59. (Available in offprint form.)

MARLER, P., "The Evolution of Visual Communication." In *Vertebrate Speciation,* Conference on Vertebrate Speciation, University of Texas. Austin: University of Texas Press, 1963.

WENNER, A. M., "Sound Communication in Honeybees." *Scientific American,* April, 1964, pp. 116-124. (Available in offprint form.)

CHAPTER 8

Genetics
and behavior

It might be expected that since ethology deals largely with innate as opposed to acquired behavior patterns, a close relationship between genetics and this branch of animal behavior should have developed. Surprisingly, this is not the case, and only in the last decade have concerted efforts been made to demonstrate the genetic bases of behavioral patterns studied by ethologists. Three major approaches to the study of behavioral genetics are being pursued. The first is to observe behavioral differences associated with single-gene mutations that affect morphological traits (*pleiotropic effects*). A second method is to analyze the inheritance of behavioral differences between inbred lines, breeds, subspecies, or even species, by *cross-matings*. The third approach is to select for specific behavioral traits in a species (*artificial selection*).

A total distinction between "innate" and "acquired" behavior patterns is extremely difficult because of the impossibility of completely separating "nature and nurture." In a sense, all behavior is genetically determined, but, except for those unique responses performed only once in an individual's lifetime (hatching, cocoon-spinning prior to pupation, fertilization in some insects, and others), one cannot be certain that experience does not play some role in the performance of a particular motor pattern. However, at least some of these difficulties can be overcome by controlling the animal's experience during ontogeny through rearing it in isolation or by physically preventing the "practicing" of some motor response to be studied later. Some biologists would restrict the use of the term "innate" to measurable and constant *differences* in behavior exhibited by individuals of different genotypes when reared under identical conditions. Thus, *species-diagnostic* differences observed under these conditions might indicate the presence of different genes affecting behavior in these forms. Additionally, some behavior patterns, although species-typical, may not be limited to a single species, but rather may be shared by one or more other species. Indeed, closely related populations may be reasonably expected to share a greater number of behavioral traits than the number by which they differ. It would appear impossible, for example, to study the genetics of the motor patterns regulating egg-hatching in birds, since this species-typical behavior occurs uniformly throughout the entire class Aves, and any mutants which failed to exhibit it under normal conditions would fail to survive.

Studies on the genetics of behavior have been attempted on a variety of animals, but certain groups are clearly more suited to this than are others. Fruit flies (*Drosophila*) have provided an important source of information, and laboratory mammals such as rats (*Rattus norvegicus*) and mice (*Mus musculus*) have also been used by behavioral geneticists. But reptiles, amphibians, fish, and birds have been almost ignored, as have the noninsect invertebrates. Selected examples from several major animal groups that represent the different lines of study mentioned above will be summarized, with emphasis on behavioral traits that are clearly of adaptive significance.

INSECTS

Among insects, the effects of single gene mutations on behavior have been best studied in *Drosophila.* By comparing the male mating success of mutant forms of *D. melanogaster,* such as yellow body color and three other sex-linked recessives, David Merrill found that most such mutants are less successful in mating than are wild type males. The female's behavior is primarily responsible for this selective mating since females normally "choose" to accept the attentions of one out of several courting males. In the instances where "male choice" appeared to be present, less vigorous males were being accepted by more receptive females. A number of mutations are known to affect mating behavior directly or indirectly. The recessive gene w, which produces white eyes, causes a reduced frequency of copulation in homozygous males by 25 per cent, and thus brings about a decreased frequency of that gene in subsequent generations. The mutation producing yellow body color affects the strength and duration of male wing vibration and the licking of the female's genitalia, which are important aspects of precopulatory display. Evidently the vibratory stimulus of the male's wings is perceived by the antennae of the female, since females lacking antennae will accept wingless males as readily as winged individuals. Yellow-bodied females are less selective than are wild type females in their choice between wild type males and yellow males.

Recent studies by H. F. Hoenigsberg and others have shown that two mutants (each carrying two mutations) of *D. melanogaster* exhibit mating preference for their own type when the other available individual in a choice situation is of wild type. This preference appeared in all courtship elements except copulation, and could serve as a basis for incipient sexual isolation. When females of wild type were given a choice, they exhibited a *homogamic* preference for wild type males, whereas wild type males either exhibited no such preference or even had *heterogamic* tendencies toward the mutant females. This experiment suggests that only a few genes can be the basis for potential reproductive isolation, which can be gradually enhanced through natural selection or more rapidly increased by artificial selection against heterogamic matings. For example, G. R. Knight and others found that it is possible to achieve a significant degree of partial sexual isolation through artificial selection in two *D. melanogaster* stocks which differed only by recessive marker genes. By allowing only the progeny of homogamic matings to survive, the rate of interbreeding between the stocks gradually declined. More recently their experiment was repeated in a modified form by Stella Crossley, who confirmed the increase in sexual isolation through anti-hybrid selection. She found that females of both genotypes exhibited a greater repulsion of heterogamic males at the end of the experiment (forty generations). Additionally, males developed a greater sensitivity to these repulsion responses by females in later generations of the experiment.

The development of homogamic matings, whether through natural or artificial selection, must in some way affect the genetic basis of male selection by females if that sex exerts a choice in mating partners, and may thus indirectly bring about a divergence in male courtship patterns. However, sexual isolation may be the result not only of courtship discrimination, but also of the relative sexual "vigor" of both sexes. It is believed that early stages of sexual isolation between strains may largely result from such differences of vigor (or thresholds of sexual response), while isolation between more distantly related groups may also involve female discrimination of quantitative or qualitative differences in male behavior patterns. Lee Ehrman, in studying various races or incipient species of *D. paulistorum,* found that female hybrids between certain of these races repelled all males. The sterile male hybrids were rejected by females of the two parental species as well as by hybrid females. Dr. Ehrman concluded that sexual isolation in *D. paulistorum* is achieved by polygenes that control sexual preferences and are additive in effect. Thus, females of hybrid origin that have a majority of chromosomes of one race are most likely to accept a male of that race. Different races show differing degrees of sexual isolation that are only weakly correlated with hybrid fertility. However, where these races overlap in nature, natural selection has evidently favored the development of sexual isolation between them.

Various examples of behavioral traits controlled by only a few genes have been found in insects. One particularly interesting case concerns the behavior of worker honeybees in removing diseased larvae from their cells. In two inbred lines of honeybee, one of which was selected for resistence to a disease called American foulbrood and the other for sensitivity to it, the workers respond differentially to the presence of diseased larvae. Workers of the resistant line first uncap the cell and then remove the affected larva, but those of the susceptible line do neither. By crossing the lines it was found that the F_1 generation is "nonhygienic" and susceptible, indicating that "hygienic" behavior (uncapping and removing) is a recessive trait. By backcrossing to the recessive genotype, four kinds of offspring can be produced. These include approximately equal proportions of bees that are hygienic, that are nonhygienic, that uncap the cell only, and that will remove larvae from uncapped cells but cannot uncap them themselves. The results of this experiment suggest that hygienic behavior is controlled by alleles on two loci that exhibit independent assortment and dominance in the typical manner of a dihybrid cross.

Several behavioral responses resulting from several genes, or *polygenic* inheritance, have been demonstrated in insects. The larval stage of the moth *Ephestia* has a behavioral varient that in spinning the pupa produces a flat mat instead of the normal type. Crosses have shown this behavior to be regulated by more than one pair of genes. Additionally, there is a wasp (*Habrobracon*) which utilizes *Ephestia* larvae for nest provisioning. Only female wasps sting larvae, since the males do not participate in nesting behavior. It has been reported that gynandromorphs (individuals having a mixture of male and female characteristics) may try to court *Ephestia* larvae and attempt to sting *Habrobracon* females! This remarkable "error" is evidently the result of a mixed constitution of sex chromosomes in the brain cells, and provides an interesting case of the genetic breakdown of adaptive behavioral traits.

Interspecific crosses between insects can sometimes be achieved under laboratory conditions, and a few behavioral genetics studies on such hybrids have been performed. Two cricket species, *Gryllus bimaculatus* and *G. campestris*, can be hybridized by using a female of the former and a male of the latter, although the reciprocal cross is prevented by behavioral isolation. Three major male courtship differences occur in the species and may be studied in the fertile hybrids. These include vibration of antennae (present only in *campestris*), body movements during copulation (also present only in *campestris*), and precopulatory stridulation sounds (produced only in *bimaculatus*, although *campestris* does raise the elytra). Apparently antennae vibration results from a single dominant gene, stridulation is regulated by a single gene with incomplete dominance, and the body movements during copulation are the result of polygenic inheritance.

NONMAMMALIAN VERTEBRATES

Probably because of the greater significance of experience in the behavior of vertebrates, it is difficult to find examples of behavioral inheritance patterns in this group that fit categories as neatly as those mentioned for insects. Among the cold-blooded vertebrates few such studies have been made, but one example is outstanding. This study concerned the genetics of sexual behavior patterns in two closely related xiphophorin fishes, which are sympatric but evidently do not naturally hydridize. These species are the swordtail (*Xiphophorus helleri*) and the platyfish (*X. maculatus*). In these viviparous fishes (the common guppy is also a representative of the general group) there is considerable sexual dimorphism, and males exhibit several elaborate courtship displays. Major behavior differences between the species occur and probably provide important isolating mechanisms. The species differ in the duration, frequency, and effectiveness of copulations, with swordtails copulating sooner after contact and for longer periods, whereas platyfish copulate more frequently and more effectively. In the F_1 hybrids, which are fertile, the copulation frequency is higher than in either parental species, but the effectiveness of insemination is intermediate. However, second generation hybrids have lower values for copulation frequency and effectiveness, and show the greatest variability in time elapsed prior to copulation. A number of different male displays were also studied. A common display of platyfish is "pecking" of the sandy substrate, a trait lacking in swordtails although they perform "nibbling" of the female's anal region. Both displays are absent in the F_1 males but occur in reduced frequency in the F_2 males and to varying degrees in the backcross combinations. A retreating movement from the female is performed by both species, although differently. In platyfish this display is called "retiring," whereas in swordtails it is referred to as "backing." The F_1 hybrids exhibit both backing and retiring, as do the F_2 males, and backcross combinations exhibit the pattern of the species to which the F_1 were crossed. Although the data did not allow for an estimate of the number of genes regulating these behavior patterns, there can be little doubt of their genetic control.

Regarding birds, relatively little can be said about possible single gene effects on behavior. However, artificial selection has provided numerous inbred lines of various domesticated species that differ markedly in behavior patterns. Although one may question the adaptive significance of some of these variations, some interesting findings have emerged.

Major differences in such traits as aggressiveness, wildness, and broodiness that have been directly or indirectly selected for can be seen in different breeds of domestic fowl (*Gallus gallus*). Available data suggest a genetic basis for mating frequency and "sex drive" in domestic fowl, and some separation of lines through selection for high and low sex drive has been achieved. When selection for separation of lines based on cumulative number of completed matings was undertaken, the resulting lines showed little difference in aggressive behavior or courting frequency (which has an agonistic component), but significant differences were present in mounting and treading frequency. Selective breeding for high and low aggressiveness in white leghorns, a social breed, has produced significant differences in only two generations. Likewise, selection against broodiness in Rhode Island reds produced a reduction in broody individuals from over 90 per cent to less than 20 per cent in five years, although the genetic basis of this hormonally related trait is still very poorly understood.

It is of equal interest to learn whether various inbred lines exhibit behavioral traits other than those which have been specifically selected for. Assortative mating within breeds of domestic fowl has been recognized for several decades. Some reports have indicated that this results from homogamic male preferences, while others suggest that the females are primarily responsible. In comparing brown and white leghorn breeds Alan Lill and D. Wood-Gush found that females do exhibit homogamy, although females of a broiler strain exhibit a heterogamic preference for brown leghorn males, which resemble ancestral jungle fowl. Evidently the females discriminate between males on the basis of physical characteristics rather than behavior differences. When males are reared with their own breed a degree of homogamic male discrimination occurs, but when reared with individuals of their own and other breeds, this discrimination, which is based on plumage characters, breaks down. Additionally, assortative mating within lines has been demonstrated in females for particular males of high sexual vigor, indicating that sexual selection can occur even at this intraline level. Assortative mating within wild populations of western grebes (*Aechmophorus occidentalis*) has also been recently found, in which two very similar plumage phases exhibit a marked degree of homogamic matings. Assortative mating likewise occurs between the "snow" and "blue" phases of snow geese (*Anser caerulescens*).

Studies on the inheritance of behavior in interspecific crosses of birds are limited. William Dilger found that the African lovebirds *Agapornis roseicollis* and *A. personata fischeri* will hybridize in captivity although the F_1's are sterile. The hybrid males are nevertheless as active sexually as are the parental species, although the females are less so. The hybrids also exhibit a partial loss of individual recognition abilities and reduced sense of territorial boundaries. Hybrids exhibit an intermediate display form between those of the parental species. One behavior pattern of special interest is the manner of carrying nesting material to the nest site. Females of *roseicollis* carry these materials, which they have cut into strips with their bills, by inserting them among the rump feathers, and thus are able to carry several pieces in a single trip. On the other hand, *personata* females carry these materials in the bill. Hybrids exhibit conflicting motor patterns, sometimes obviously attempting to tuck the materials in the rump feathers but never successfully doing so. After several fruitless efforts to tuck the materials, females sometimes eventually fly off with a single piece of material in the bill. The initial hybrid efficiency at carrying this material in the bill is about 6 per cent, improving to about 40 per cent after two months. After three years, about 90 per cent of the materials are successfully carried, and finally after four years, the females are nearly as efficient as pure *personata*. This slow improvement suggests a very limited ability for modifying these innate motor patterns through experience, although the sterility of the hybrids prevents an analysis of the genetic basis for this behavior.

Interspecific hybrids among various species of dabbling ducks (*Anas*) provides a second source of information on the inheritance of species-typical avian behavior patterns. A surprising degree of interspecific fertility exists among duck hybrids, even among such different-appearing birds as the mallard and pintail. These species very rarely hybridize under normal conditions, yet in captivity they do so fairly readily. The hybrids are evidently fully fertile, so that backcrosses and second generation birds can be obtained. Females of the parental species do not differ greatly in plumage or displays, but the males exhibit considerable differences in these traits. For example, both species perform one display ("grunt-whistle") nearly identically, and another ("head-up-tail-up") with only minor differences. However, only the mallard performs the "down-up" display, and only the pintail performs the "burp." "Nod-swimming" is frequent and conspicuous in the mallard, but occurs in only rudimentary form in pintails. The F_1 males are essentially intermediate between the parentals in their displays; the down-up is lacking, and burping and nod-swimming are performed in reduced form. The grunt-whistle and head-up-tail-up are both frequent and like the parentals'. Some F_2 males are distinctly mallard-like in plumage, and others are relatively pintail-like. Furthermore, the mallard-like males perform mallard-like displays (down-up present, nod-swimming well developed), and the same applies to the pintail-like males (burp well developed, nod-swimming rudimentary). These facts suggest a common inheritance of plumage and behavioral traits of the two species. Some of the displays are evidently inherited in all-or-none fashion (down-up) and thus are probably dependent on only a very few genes, and others (nod-swimming, head-up-tail-up) show differing degrees of intermediacy between the extreme forms. It would appear that although the inheritance of the behavioral and plumage traits may vary in complexity, they generally are under fairly simple genetic control. The generally intermediate appearance and motor patterns of the F_1 and typical F_2 males probably prevent their mating success in choice situations; in addition, they appear to have a reduced display frequency and a greater tendency to form homosexual attachments among themselves.

In the more closely related black duck (*A. rubripes*), hybridization with mallards is much more common in the area of range overlap. In these two species the male displays are qualitatively identical, although plumage differences are present. Furthermore, the F_1 hybrids must sometimes obtain mates under wild conditions, since there is a complete spectrum of plumage types between mallards and black ducks to be found in wild populations. However, a high degree of assortative mating can still be demonstrated, as shown by a relatively low hybrid frequency (less than 5 per cent) in the areas of primary contact.

MAMMALS

Paradoxically, although the mammals are probably least suited to studies of behavioral genetics, the greatest amount of information has accumulated for this group of vertebrates. Numerous behavioral effects of monogenic mutations have been described. Over fifty such mutations have been found in laboratory mice, most of which are associated with neurological defects and resulting changes in locomotory behavior. Mutants which produce "waltzing," "circling," "jittery," and similar aberrant movements are examples. Similarly, both wild and tame strains of rats and mice have been developed, and their different responses have been shown to have a genetic basis. Likewise, measures of "emotionality" in rats and mice have been made and similarly found to be genetically based, but not necessarily correlated with wildness. Jan Bruell has performed extensive comparisons of behavioral traits of inbred strains of mice, and has made various crosses between them. In comparing the parental and "hybrid" populations for two behavioral traits, exploratory activity and running in activity wheels, he found that the hybrids usually outscored the parentals, thus exhibiting *behavioral heterosis*. Of thirty-one hybrid groups, twenty-one scored higher than the higher scoring inbred parent for explority activity and only one scored lower than the lower scoring parent. Crosses between more distantly related parents showed a higher degree of heterosis than those between more closely related ones. However, the reactions of the hybrids to various physiological tests were intermediate between the parentals. Dr. Bruell has suggested that heterotic inheritance of traits is typical of those which have adaptive value and have been subjected to selection, whereas "neutral" traits do not exhibit heterosis.

Similarly, various workers have performed extensive breeding experiments between breeds of dogs that differ in social behavior patterns. In comparing over thirty behavioral variables tested among five dog breeds, John Scott and John Fuller concluded that all but one showed significant differences among the breeds, and that an average of over 25 per cent of the total variation observed in the traits studied could be attributed to breed differences. At least another 12 per cent could be attributed to matings within breeds, and thus is also genetic. In crosses between one barking breed (cocker spaniel) and a relatively quiet breed (basenji), the F_1 generation is much like the cocker spaniel. The F_2 individuals show more variation, but a fairly good fit was achieved by the assumption of a single dominant factor controlling this character.

Mammals are doubtless influenced strongly by individual experience, and ecological adaptations such as habitat preferences presumably are based on a complex interplay of numerous inherited and acquired factors. However, there is evidence that behavioral niche adaptations may be almost as much genetically determined in mammals as are such structural niche adaptations as tooth structure and limb proportions. For example, two subspecies of deermice, *Peromyscus maniculatus bairdi* and *P. m. gracilis*, respectively occupy grasslands and forests of central North America. When individuals of these two races are raised in the laboratory, the grassland race *bairdi* exhibits a marked preference (in terms of total time spent and locations selected for various activities) for an artificial grassland, and the forest race prefers an artificial forest. In F_1 hybrids between these races there is a definite preference for the grassland habitat. It has also been shown that laboratory-reared individuals of tree-dwelling subspecies of *Peromyscus* tend to climb more steeply inclined planes than do grassland forms. Recent experiments by Stanley Wecker have extended these earlier findings. He determined that laboratory stock of *bairdi* some twelve to twenty generations removed from wild grassland stock prefer grassland to wood environments in less than half of the criteria used. However, wild stock *bairdi* reared in a woods environment still preferred grassland when tested later. The hereditary grassland preference of wild-stock *bairdi* thus cannot be blocked by rearing in the woods, but on the other hand it was found that this preference can be reinforced by early experience in a grassland situation. Although the laboratory stock of *bairdi* had essentially lost their innate grassland preferences, they still exhibited reinforced preferences for it when reared in grassland, whereas woods-reared *bairdi* of the same stock also failed to develop a preference for woods. Presumably, the inherited habitat preference of this subspecies developed slowly, as mutations favoring a survival in grassland habitat supplemented and eventually largely replaced the learned preference for it. The actual process by which inherited adaptations gradually replace acquired responses (the *Baldwin effect*) is still debated, but must play an important role in the evolution of behavioral habitat adaptations, to be considered next.

SUGGESTED READING

BLISS, E. L. (ed.), *Roots of Behavior*. New York: Harper & Bros., 1962, 339 pp.

CASPARI E., "Genetic Basis of Behavior." In ROE, A., and SIMPSON, G. G., (eds.), *Behavior and Evolution*. New Haven, Conn.: Yale University Press, 1962, pp. 103-127.

CLARK, E.; ARONSON L.; and GORDON, M., "Mating Behavior Patterns in Two Sympatric Species of Xiphophorin Fishes: Their Inheritance and Significance." In *American Museum of Natural History Bulletin* 103:135-226, 1954.

DILGER, W. C., "The Behavior of Lovebirds." *Scientific American*, January, 1962, pp. 88-98.

FULLER, J. L., and THOMPSON, W. R., *Behavior Genetics*, New York: John Wiley & Sons, Inc., 1960, 396 pp.

HAFEZ, E. S. E. (ed.), *The Behavior of Domestic Animals*. London: Balliére, Tindall & Cox, Ltd., 1962, 619 pp.

LORENZ, K. Z., "The Evolution of Behavior." *Scientific American*, December, 1958, pp. 67-68.

SCOTT, J. P., and FULLER, J. L., *Genetics and the Social Behavior of the Dog*. Chicago: University of Chicago Press, 1965, 468 pp.

SHARPE, R. S., and JOHNSGARD, P. A., "Inheritance of Behavioral Characters in F$_2$ Mallard x Pintail (*Anas platyrhynchos* L. x *Anas acuta* L.) Hybrids." Behaviour 27: pp. 259-272, 1966.

WECKER, S. C., "Habitat Selection." *Scientific American*, October, 1964, pp. 109-116. (Available in offprint form.)

CHAPTER 9

Ecology and behavior

In considering the ecology of animals it is important to keep in mind the distinction between the conditions imposed by the environment and the behavioral and structural adjustments of a species to that environment. Thus, a species' *niche* represents its adaptive adjustments to a particular environmental *habitat*, which may also support other species having similar or different niches. The capacity of a given environmental area to support populations of animals having the same or similar niches is its *carrying capacity*, which may be greater or less than the *saturation point*, or maximum density, of an individual species. The saturation point reflects such species-typical behavioral criteria as territorial and home range requirements, or individual distance tolerances in those species lacking territories. The saturation point may even be affected by the presence of other species having overlapping niche requirements so that there results *competitive exclusion* from the same habitat. Finally, a species may have a minimum tolerable density, or *survival threshold*, below which it is unable to survive in a habitat for behavioral, physiological, or genetic reasons. The diverse means by which a species is thus behaviorally and structurally adapted to exploit a particular habitat at population levels that do not fluctuate beyond its saturation point or below its survival threshold, and which avoid severe interspecific competition, represent the species' *ecological adaptations.*

As described in the preceding chapter, the adaptations of a species to its habitat are likely to include factors dependent upon both heredity and experience. In its broadest interpretation, a species' ecological niche thus includes innate and acquired environmental adjustments such as foraging adaptations, habitat preferences, periodicity of activity, and predator or prey adaptations. Frequently, competition-reducing adaptations are present that are too subtle to measure easily, and indirect measurements may be required, such as undertaking comparative studies in different locations where populations are low or where potential competitors are absent. Behavioral adaptations for avoiding or reducing competition are of two general types, those associated with reducing *intraspecific competition* for such things as food, nest-sites and other density-related factors, and those related to avoiding *interspecific competition* from species with overlapping niche adaptations. Other behavioral adaptations not directly related to competition may be concerned with more efficient *adjustments to particular habitats*, possibly allowing for reduced mortality and larger populations per unit area. These three kinds of adaptations will be considered in turn.

INTRASPECIFIC COMPETITION—REDUCING ADAPTATIONS

Intraspecific competition is frequently prevented or reduced in vertebrates by *territorial behavior*, which brings about a spacing-out of individuals or pairs and restricts direct contacts and competition to the boundaries of the territory. Where feeding grounds are some distance from the breeding area, (as in sea birds) or are rich but restricted to a relatively small area (such as a marsh), foraging areas are frequently excluded for the defended territory but are part of the larger and undefended *home range*. Rarely, territories may include only a restricted display area for the males, and in such cases territoriality cannot effectively serve as a spacing mechanism for populations. Where territories are restricted to the area around the nest, adaptations for the recognition of nest site, mate, and young are needed. It is not surprising, therefore, that "greeting" displays and nest-relief displays between mates are well developed in such birds as penguins, herons, gulls, and albatrosses, since "mistakes" in mate recognition could easily lead to the destruction of the nest or young.

In species lacking mutually exclusive territories, a considerable degree of habitat sharing is frequent. Social organization may still be achieved by maintenance of *individual distances* or by *dominance relationships,* as occurs in howler monkeys and baboons. The average home range of a baboon troop may be fifteen square miles, within which a "core area" of about three square miles exists. Core areas include sleeping trees, food, water, and sites of refuge from large predators. Adjoining troops do not fight over home ranges and these frequently overlap, but core areas do not.

Nonterritorial species, or those which defend extremely restricted territories, are likely to build up into enormous concentrations in rich foraging areas. The incredibly dense colonies of sea birds along various coastlines are too large to attempt counting, but the northern hemisphere thick-billed murre (*Uria lomvia*) has been estimated to total 40, possibly even 80, million individuals. Two species of Peruvian guano birds, a cormorant (*Phalacrocorax bougainvillei*) and a booby (*Sula variegata*), may each reach populations of 30 to 40 million individuals in good years. Possibly the red-billed weaver (*Quelea quelea*) of Africa is even more abundant than any of these; single trees may support up to 5,000 nests, and flocks estimated at 40 million birds have been seen. For such species nesting space may be an important limiting factor in population size, and individual distances often are restricted to the maximum point a bird can reach and peck its neighbor without moving off its own nest site. But murre pairs may even be forced to occupy nest sites no larger than half a square foot in the heart of nesting colonies, and densities of from twenty-eight to thirty-seven nesting birds per square meter have been reported! After disturbances, these birds return to their nests as soon as possible; otherwise, they would soon lose them to others. Amazingly, such tiny nesting sites may be returned to in following years by the same pair.

Where populations of a species are high, and food supplies are limited, various means of reducing intraspecific competition for food might be expected. Theoretically two possible means include foraging *differences in different age groups* of a species, and foraging *differences in the two sexes*. There is still only a limited amount of evidence regarding these possibilities. Food-intake differences between young and adult animals may be primarily a reflection of different nutritional needs. However, a separation of foraging areas by reproductively immature and adult animals, with similar food consumption by the two groups, might be regarded as evidence of such an age-related competition-reducing mechanism. This might occur in gulls and other species with prolonged periods of sexual immaturity; first-year ducks of species that do not breed until their second year typically avoid the crowded breeding grounds and remain in larger water areas.

Sexual differences in foraging behavior may be associated with anatomical as well as behavioral differences between the sexes, or only the latter. A classic example of structural sexual dimorphism associated with foraging differences in the sexes occurred in the extinct New Zealand huia (*Neomorpha acutirostris*). The male of this crow-sized bird had a relatively straight and strong bill, whereas that of the female was longer and decurved. The birds evidently foraged in pairs, with the male ripping bark with his stout bill, and the female extracting insects from exposed crevices with her more slender bill. Many woodpeckers exhibit greater sexual dimorphism in bill length than in other bodily measurement, and this difference has been regarded as evidence for different foraging niches. It has recently been found that the female hairy woodpecker (*Dendrocopos villosus*) typically extracts the more superficial insects from trees, rather than obtaining them by deeper excavation as do males. This sexual difference results in a measurable separation of foraging areas between the sexes. This separation has also been observed in the red-cockaded woodpecker (*D. borealis*), and a similar segregation of sexes in wintering flocks of various birds has been found. Thus, male ptarmigan (*Lagopus* spp.) winter at higher elevations than do females, and males of various migratory species winter farther north than females and juveniles. However, these differences may simply reflect a greater attachment to breeding territories in males, or possibly a greater tolerance of colder temperatures in large individuals.

INTERSPECIFIC COMPETITION—REDUCING ADAPTATIONS

It is probable that no two species occupy exactly identical niches in the same area over an indefinite period of time (the principle of competitive exclusion), but it is known that continuing interspecific competition for similar niches or certain aspects of niches is a fact. There are various morphological and behavioral adaptations for reducing such interspecific competition while at the same time exploiting the available habitat to the fullest degree. The Galapagos finches (Geospizinae) are a classic example.

The Galapagos finches comprise a group of fourteen species that are restricted to these islands off the coast of Ecuador. The islands vary greatly in size and distance from one another, and aside from the finches exhibit a depauperate fauna of small birds. The number of finch species found on the various island ranges from one on the smallest outlying islands to ten on the larger central islands. On such large islands as Indefatigable, the resident species include one with a bill that is short, narrow, and warbler-like (*Certhidea olivacea*), and that is associated with foraging for insects on leafy vegetation. Heavier, grasping bills with biting tips are typical of species (*Camarhynchus* spp.) having primarily insectivorous diets and foraging by hunting for insects hidden in plant tissues. Extremely heavy crushing bills are found on those species (*Geospiza spp.*) having primarily vegetarian diets of seeds. The five species of *Geospiza* found on this island themselves show a spectrum of bill variations from extremely large and heavy (*G. magnirostris*) to relatively long and weak (*G. scandens*). According to Robert Bowman these two species forage respectively on very hard, generally large seeds, and on moderately hard seeds as well as plant tissues and nectar. Although interspecific competition is obviously reduced by these variations in structure and behavior, Dr. Bowman doubts that competition played as significant a role in evolving these differences and determining present-day distribution patterns as other biologists have suggested. Rather, the differences that now occur are largely the result of structural and behavioral adjustments to local conditions that evolved during periods of isolation. In subsequent periods of sympatry these existing differences may well have served to reduce competition and possibly were further perfected. On the smaller outlying islands where few species exist, habitats utilized by certain species may be more diverse or slightly different from those which they occupy on the central islands.

A number of other instances of *ecological segregation* are known where two species occur in different habitats or share different parts of the same habitat in areas of overlap, but expand their ecological niche to include that of the other species where it is absent. In England and Europe the willow tit (*Parus atricapillus*) is widespread but is generally restricted to swampy forests, but in North America, where it is called the black-capped chickadee, the species has a much broader habitat spectrum. The explanation appears to be that in England four or five other species directly compete with it over much of its range, and presumably restrict it to the habitat it is best adapted to, whereas in North American interspecific competition from other species of *Parus* is nearly absent. Where the species does overlap in breeding distribution with the brown-capped chickadee (*P. hudsonicus*), the latter is usually found in moist coniferous habitats and the black-capped chickadee occurs in the higher and more open forests. Closely related species of *Parus* in the United States appear to replace one another ecologically in different regions having similar forest habitats.

It has been suggested that the stable and diverse habitats of the tropics, which support a wide variety of niches, may have a larger proportion of avian species which are "masters-of-one-trade," and the ecologically more uniform temperate zones may be occupied by more "jacks-of-all-trades," birds which are less behaviorally stereotyped and thus have broader ecological niches. But even temperate species may exhibit a surprising degree of adaptation to specific foraging niches. A study by Joe Marshall on the birds of the pine-oak woodlands of the southwestern states and Mexico provides an example.

Dr. Marshall analyzed the typical foraging niches of over eighty bird species that occur in the pine-oak community, and whose foraging niches are related to the vegetation. Of these species that are largely insectivorous he found that some typically forage in the foliage and twigs, others on branches and trunks, and yet others in the foliage and air. Some of the birds within each of these categories foraged primarily in pines, others in oaks, and still others in different trees or brush. Certain closely related species, such as bluebirds (*Sialia* spp.) and vireos (*Vireo* spp.), appeared to exhibit competitive exclusion. Thus, the bluebirds had complementary distribution patterns over the study area, and the vireos foraged in different levels of the same tree or in different trees. An equivalent *locational segregation* of foraging niches has been observed among various New World warblers (Parulidae), in which both vertical and horizontal restrictions of foraging overlap appear to be present.

Temporal segregation of activity may also serve to reduce competition between species having similar niches. Such segregation may be based on diel activity patterns (differences in diurnal, nocturnal, or crepuscular activity) or on different seasonal patterns of activity. Differences that may be most pronounced include the timing of the breeding period, when adequate food supplies are a prerequisite for reproductive success.

BEHAVIORAL ADAPTATIONS TO PARTICULAR HABITATS

The behavioral adaptations which a species evolves and which enable it best to survive in a given community are often difficult to assess. Most animal species are not closely tied to particular community types, partly because of their mobility but also because animals usually do not depend directly upon a single plant species for their survival. Rather, vertebrates, at least, usually respond to a general life form, or vegetational physiognomy. For example, many grassland species of birds are common to such diverse North American vegetational types as tall-grass prairie, short-grass plains, bunch-grass prairie, and California annual

99

grassland. These plant communities have very different dominant grass species but share such breeding birds as the western meadowlark (*Sturnella neglecta*), grasshopper sparrow (*Ammodramus savannarum*) and horned lark (*Eremophila alpestris*), and the last also breeds in open areas of various vegetational zones as high as alpine tundra.

In temperate and arctic communities food chains are often short and moderately simple. Small or large herbivores of a few species crop the relatively homogeneous vegetation and in turn may be preyed upon by only a few kinds of predators. Such direct relationships between the major ecological "producers" and "consumers" result in strong interdependence, and population "cycles" are especially prevalent in such situations. This kind of fluctuating economy has been described in a number of arctic food chains. In such species there are often massive emigrations when the herbivore population outgrows its food supply, and the animals must either move to new areas or starve. The nearly constant migrations of caribou (*Rangifer*) serve to avoid overharvesting the limited food resources.

In tropical communities it is uncommon to find large numbers of vertebrates of a single species. The large herds of African ungulates are usually of mixed composition, and mixed flocks of birds are typical of the tropics of both hemispheres. In studies of Neotropical mixed species flocks, Martin Moynihan has concluded that these may have evolved as social bonds gradually developed between a species having a high degree of intraspecific gregariousness and one or more species not so gregarious. The former species may then serve as an active or passive nucleus for the attraction of additional species. Various finches and tanagers are typical nuclear species in Central America, and those species that serve as active nuclear species have broader ranges than related ones that are passive nuclear species or do not participate in mixed flocks. There would thus appear to be an evolutionary advantage in the formation of mixed flocks. Many tropical species have highly specialized foraging adaptations such as nectar sucking, and must be almost constantly moving as they search for the scattered food plants they depend upon. The advantages of moving in mixed flocks, in terms of reduced competition and having a common predator warning system, are readily apparent. Likewise, baboons frequently associate with impala gazelles (*Aepycerus melampus*), whose superior senses of smell and hearing complement the eyesight of the baboon.

Sometimes birds associate with wild mammals on a commensal or mutualistic basis, such as by foraging on the insects stirred up by the

larger mammals, or by removing and eating external parasites imbedded in their skin. In the Philippine Islands a species of drongo (*Dicrurus*) is known as the "sentinel of the monkeys," and in Africa other drongos follow herds of elephants or monkey troops and forage on disturbed insects. A similar association between a trogon (*Trogon massena*) and monkey bands has been observed in Panama.

The mutualistic association between numerous marine fish and their "cleaners" has only recently become fully appreciated. It appears that a surprising number of large fish inhabiting coral reefs are regularly tended by smaller cleaner fish, such as wrasse (Labridae), which remove parasites or diseased tissue from the skin of these fish. Cleaning fish may even swim with impunity into the open mouths of such carnivores as barracuda (*Sphyraena*) to remove debris from around their teeth. These larger fish will regularly return to certain "cleaning stations" to be attended to, in much the same manner that a human regularly visits his barber or dentist, and may even have to "wait in line" for service. At least twenty-six species of fish, including several wrasses, are regular cleaners. Cleaner fish are often brightly colored and strikingly patterned; presumably these markings evolved as a means of easy recognition. However, one species of blenny (*Aspidontus*) has also evolved a striped, wrasse-like pattern and, when an unsuspecting "patient" approaches, the blenny attacks with its saber-like teeth — a fine example of a "stolen" signaling device.

Some additional generalizations can be made about behavioral adjustments to typical terrestrial community types that occur from the arctic to the tropics. Among arctic and alpine birds and mammals it is common to find behavioral and physiological adaptations that favor a rapid completion of the breeding cycle. Nesting, fledging, and molting periods are speeded up markedly over those of temperate zone relatives. Like prairie birds, arctic tundra species frequently perform flight songs and have associated visual flight displays. Relatively few arctic songbirds utilize seeds to any degree; even finchlike birds largely consume the abundant insects which they capture during the long days of the arctic summer. Since insect food for the nestling is usually not limiting, clutch sizes in arctic species are often large, but time does not permit the rearing of multiple broods. Except near the sea, where food may be nearly unlimited, colonial nesting and dense breeding concentrations of birds are not typical. Rather, upland tundra is relatively poor in both number of breeding bird species and density, which is frequently less than thirty total pairs per hundred acres.

Grasslands are largely occupied by herbivores that may be cursorial or saltatorial, and are often highly gregarious. The smaller mammals frequently hibernate during winter, estivate during hot and dry periods, or both. Some prairie birds are relatively cursorial and exhibit protective coloration, especially in females. Aerial territorial displays are common in grassland birds, and are often associated with conspicuous wing or tail markings. A much larger number of seed-eaters than insect-eaters is typical; in North America the "sparrows" (Emberizidae) and omnivorous "blackbirds" (Icteridae) are well represented, whereas the warbler family Parulidae is often lacking in representatives.

In desert communities, nocturnal activity patterns are the rule, and the daylight hours are often spent in the shade or in burrows. Insectivorous birds are frequent, but seed eaters and carnivores are less common. Periods of reproduction may be restricted to the sometimes erratic rainy seasons. Since plant life is scarce and varied, with little or no ecological dominance, concentrations of single animal species are not prevalent. North American deserts sometimes support somewhat larger numbers of bird species and densities than do grassland and tundra communities, at times up to 150 total pairs per hundred acres, but in the almost complete absence of plants the bird populations may be nil.

Temperate coniferous forests are similar in animal constitution and adaptations to northern hardwood forests, but usually considerably fewer plant species are present and the fauna is also generally poorer. Seeds of conifers are an important food source for certain birds which may have specialized behavior and bill structures for extracting them (as do crossbills and grosbeaks). In temperate hardwood forests, with their abundant nuts and acorns, many birds and mammals are adept at nut-cracking and practice caching of nut supplies. Acoustic signals are usually important to forest-dwelling animals, and numerous forest birds and mammals have strong voices. Tree-climbing and tree-nesting adaptations are common in both birds and mammals. Insect-eating birds are abundant and in North America include several representatives of the warblers, tyrant flycatchers, thrushes, and titmice. Uniform stands of mature temperate forest frequently support an estimated 100 to 400 pairs of breeding birds per hundred acres.

Tropical evergreen forests differ considerably from temperate forests in their constitution, having evolved in a highly constant climate with little yearly variation in temperature, radiation, and rainfall. Thus, many species of plants and animals with specialized ecological requirements can exist here, and both plant and animal populations tend to be highly varied, with no ecological dominance. Such highly unusual foraging adaptations as pollen-eating and fungus-eating are possible here, and although the total animal biomass per unit area may be not much higher than in temperate regions, a far greater species diversity is typical. From 70 to 100 or more bird species per hundred acres have been reported, with usual densities of 500 or more pairs.

In common with temperate-forest species, tropical-forest vertebrates rely heavily on acoustic communication. Most of the birds of the lower levels are dull in coloration, and only those of the forest edge or canopy layers often show the bright coloration generally associated with tropical birds. There is a great deal of horizontal stratification in species composition and activity. Many species of birds build pendent nests at the tips of branches; no doubt such nests are less susceptible to the numerous arboreal predators than are open cup nests placed on larger branches. Most of the mammals are highly arboreal, rarely coming out of the trees, but a surprising number are also excellent swimmers, and able to cross the numerous streams associated with lowland rain-forest.

Behavioral adaptations to special habitats other than the ones described above are also common. Unusual nesting sites, such as cavities or cliff ledges, may require the evolution of behavioral adaptations directly related to survival problems imposed by such sites. A study by the English ethologist Esther Cullen, on the cliff-nesting kittiwake (*Rissa tridactyla*), is an excellent example. Unlike the more typical ground-nesting gulls, the kittiwake has relatively low predation pressures. On the other hand, there is a serious danger of the eggs or young falling out of the nest and being destroyed. Moreover, nest sites are restricted and nesting materials have to be brought in. Mrs. Cullen has shown how these habitat requirements and selective pressures have greatly modified the behavior of the kittiwake and account for many of the "aberrant" behavioral and morphological characteristics that distinguish it from the more typical gulls. Important supporting evidence for her hypothesis has been provided by a recent study of the Galapagos swallow-tailed gull (*Larus furcatus*). Although also a cliff-nesting species, it often nests at much lower heights and on less steep inclines than does the kittiwake. Of seventeen morphological and behavioral characters which appear to be adaptive to conditions common to both species, the swallow-tailed gull resembles the kittiwake in most, six are like the ground-nesting species, and one is intermediate. Similarly, studies of a cliff-nesting tern, the black noddy (*Anous tenuirostris*), have revealed behavioral adaptations similar to those of the kittiwake and distinct from the typical terns. Obviously, the taxonomic evaluation of morphological structures associated with cliff-nesting in these species and which make them "aberrant" must be made in the light of their probable ecological significance.

Recent studies by John Crook have also emphasized the importance of ecology in shaping the evolution of behavioral traits among the African weaver birds (Ploceinae). Male advertisement display in these birds typically centers upon the nest constructed by the male prior to mating. Nest form, which is adapted to the ecological nest site, may vary and thus may modify orientation of the male's nest advertisement displays. In nests with side entrances, upright displays are typical, whereas inverted displays are performed by males having nest entrances underneath. Furthermore, differences in the amount of vegetational cover around the nest may influence the location of the male displays. Related species living in a variety of degrees of dispersion during breeding show an associated range of pair-formation behavior patterns. Probably since food supplies are often limited during the prolonged breeding season, primarily insectivorous species inhabiting open or dense forest and savannah areas tend to be monogamous. Such species lack dimorphism and often nest in solitary pairs. In these species male precopulatory displays precede or coincide with nest advertisement display by the male. However, primarily granivorous species of grasslands typically breed in neighborhoods or colonies, are usually polygynous (food supplies are abundant at the time of breeding, which follows rain) and are sexually dimorphic. Males of these species exhibit aerial advertisement displays of the territory rather than the nest, preceding precopulatory display in the territory. Clearly the ecology of each species has played a major role in shaping male behavior and plumage characteristics, both of which might be readily misinterpreted by a taxonomist unfamiliar with the differences in the ecology of these birds. But certain interspecific homologies in the displays can be detected in this group of birds, and the next chapter will consider the potential use of such behavioral characters for taxonomic purposes.

SUGGESTED READING

BOWMAN, R. I., "Morphological Differentiation and Adaptation in the Galapagos Finches." (University of California Publications in Zoology, Vol. 58). Berkeley: University of California Press, 1961, 302 pp.

CROOK, J. H., "The Evolution of Social Organization and Visual Communication in the Weaver Birds (*Ploceinae*)," *Behaviour* Supplement X, 1964, 178 pp.

DIXON, R. L., "Habitat Distribution and Niche Relationships in North American Species of *Parus*." In *Vertebrate Speciation*, Conference on Vertebrate Speciation, University of Texas. Austin: University of Texas Press, 1961, 642 pp.

KLOPFER, P. H., *Behavioral Aspects of Ecology*. Englewood Cliffs, N. J.: Prentice-Hall, Inc., 1962, 171 pp. (Available in paperback.)

LIMBAUGH, CONRAD, "Cleaning Symbiosis." *Scientific American*, August, 1961. (Available in offprint form.)

MARSHALL, J. T., JR., "Birds of the Pine-Oak Woodland in Southern Arizona and Adjacent Mexico." *Pacific Coast Avifauna*, No. 32, 1957, 125 pp.

MOYNIHAN, M., "The Organization and Probable Evolution of Some Mixed Species Flocks of Neotropical Birds." *Smithsonian Miscellaneous Collections* 143: 1-140, 1962.

ORIANS, G. H., "The Ecology of Blackbird (*Agelaius*) Social Systems." *Ecological Monographs* 31: 285-312, 1961.

SMITH, R. L. *Ecology and Field Biology*. New York: Harper and Roe, Publishers, 1966, 686 pp.

TINBERGEN, N., "Behavior and Natural Selection," In *Ideas in Modern Biology*. Garden City, N. Y.: Natural History Press, 1965, pp. 519-542.

CHAPTER 10

Taxonomy and behavior

A major function of taxonomy is to reflect as accurately as possible the evolutionary relationships within a group of organisms and, in the process, provide a stable nomenclature that will establish a set of valid names for species and groups reflecting these relationships. Such early behaviorists as Charles Whitman and Oskar Heinroth recognized that bird species can be described behaviorally as well as morphologically, and that behavioral differences or similarities may provide a clue to evolutionary affinities. More recently, ethologists have applied this concept to an increasing number of animal groups and, usually in conjunction with morphological data, have evaluated their findings against the existing taxonomic arrangements of the groups.

The use of behavior, like other taxonomic characters, requires the collection of data on homologous features that can be compared for individuals, species, or larger groups, and which allow for either *discrimination* among such groups ("splitting" characters) or the *association* of related groups ("lumping" characters). Data on innate and species-typical behavior can thus be applied taxonomically, although the application of such information must be given a weighting appropriate to its evolutionary significance. Like morphological characters, behavior is subject to parallel, convergent, and divergent evolution; convergent or divergent behavioral adaptations are especially frequent in foraging behavior and the morphological structures associated with foraging behavior. Therefore, the importance of ecology in directly affecting certain aspects of behavior cannot be overemphasized, and the early attitude that innate behavior associated with reproduction is totally free of adaptive influences must certainly be rejected. Ecological adaptations can somewhat indirectly influence specific patterns of reproductive behavior, as shown in the last chapter, thus precautions in applying this source of behavioral information must also be taken.

In theory, the utilization of behavior should be possible for defining any taxonomic category, or *taxon*, from subspecies to phylum. However, the use of behavior is especially valuable at the species level, since at this level interspecies differences in reproductive behavior frequently directly act as important isolating mechanisms. In the case of *sibling species* that cannot be readily distinguished morphologically, patterns of reproductive or food-getting behavior are often highly differentiated and may serve to separate such forms. At higher levels, such as those of the genus and subfamily, the presence or absence of homologous behavioral patterns can often be used as a criterion of relationship, particularly when they are not directly involved in achieving reproductive isolation or niche adaptations. The presence of such a uniform pattern throughout a group of species may indicate that it is taxonomically "conservative," as opposed to the relatively varied behavior patterns that maintain species isolation and reduce interspecific competition.

In many waterfowl (Anatidae), male pair-forming displays vary widely within closely related groups and, together with male plumage patterns, presumably provide the major reproductive isolating mechanisms. In contrast, pair-maintaining displays, and displays associated with copulation, are much more uniform within higher taxonomic groupings, since these probably serve primarily for synchronizing the pair's reproductive cycles and in reducing nonsexual responses toward the mate. Behavior patterns such as bathing, preening, stretching, shaking, and other maintenance and locomotory activities exhibit little variation throughout the entire family, and evidently represent functional, unritualized responses relatively free of direct pressures for divergence. Such patterns provide important motor bases for ritualized signaling behavior in waterfowl, and displays derived from various "comfort" movements are especially prevalent in this family.

The use of behavior for taxonomic purposes is certainly most valuable in those groups relying largely on instinctive patterns rather than on acquired responses, but a surprisingly wide range of animal groups, including mammals, have been studied by behavioral taxonomists. Thus, the typical cats (Felidae) and civets (Viverridae) have been compared behaviorally, and variations in prey-catching behavior have been found to have phylogenetic significance. The five species of the African ungulate genus *Tragelaphus* have been found to be quite distinct behaviorally from the typical bovine ruminants. All the genera of the rodent family Heteromyidae have been investigated by John Eisenberg, who reported that such basic activities as digging, food gathering and storage, washing, feeding, and maternal care are very similar in all species, but locomotory patterns exhibit evolutionary trends ranging from quadripedal to bipedal methods. Social behavior patterns have basic similarities but exhibit some species differences, with elaborate and stereotyped displays in certain species.

Several families or subfamilies of birds have been studied by ethologists, although not always specifically for taxonomic purposes. The waterfowl family Anatidae is perhaps the best known, with over 90 per cent of the nearly 150 species having been studied by one or more ethologists. The work of Niko Tinbergen, Martin Moynihan, and others on over half of the approximately thirty-five species of gulls in the family Laridae has shown that a great deal more similarity in reproductive behavior exists among these species than among ducks, although species-typical differences can be found. For example, pair-forming behavior in gulls varies hardly at all in related species, and exhibits strong similarities within taxonomic subgroups of the family. The taxonomically difficult finchlike birds have proven popular for behavioral study, partly because of their adaptability to captivity. Behavioral analyses are therefore now available for a substantial proportion of the Old World waxbills (Estrildinae), weaver birds (Ploceinae), and African widow birds (Viduinae), some of the tree finches (Carduelinae), and various American sparrows and European buntings (Emberizinae). Such studies have suggested new arrangements of these groups into taxonomic categories that appear to be more realistic than those based on anatomical data.

Application of behavior to the taxonomy of reptiles and amphibians is more limited, but recent studies on various species and genera of lizards in the family Iguanidae by Charles Carpenter and others indicate that the male "challenge" displays are species-specific and may provide a basis for species recognition by females. Generic, specific, and even racial variations occur in the challenge display that can be used to demonstrate taxonomic relationships, but other basic patterns of male behavior (especially those associated with copulation) are the same or very similar throughout the family. The classic studies by G. Kingsley Noble also indicated that related species and genera of lizards and salamanders may exhibit almost identical courtship patterns. Noble also observed similarities in courtship between the closely related snake genera *Storeria* and *Thamnophis,* and described how courtship patterns in snakes differ at higher taxonomic levels. Unlike lizards, olfaction is of great importance in the reproduction of snakes, and in many species skin secretions allow for both species and sexual recognition.

Application of behavioral information, especially vocalization patterns, has been made by various zoologists, including W. Frank Blair, for studying species isolation in such anuran genera as *Bufo* and *Hyla.* Three families of fish have received particular attention from ethologists: the pair-forming Cichlidae, the bubble-nesting Anabantidae, and the nest-building sticklebacks (Gasterosteidae). Representatives of these families are known to exhibit species-typical behavior patterns which are very similar among closely related species. In studying six species of glandulocaudine fishes of the family Characidae, Keith Nelson found behavioral evidence supporting the view that this morphologically diverse group is of monophyletic rather than polyphyletic origin.

A number of investigators have found behavioral data of great value in taxonomic studies of insects. This has proven especially true for the social and solitary Hymenoptera, and also for species utilizing acoustic isolating mechanisms. Howard Evans was able to define the spider wasp family Pompilidae by five behavioral criteria that serve as well as any morphological characters. About 200 out of a total of roughly 2,000 species of crickets (Gryllidae) have now been studied behaviorally by taxonomists. Likewise, the courtship behavior of over 100 species of *Drosophila* has been studied, allowing for important conclusions on the taxonomy and evolution of behavior in this group. A study by H. S. Barber on the flashing behavior of eighteen species and subspecies of fireflies (*Photuris*) revealed no less than twelve undescribed forms, proving the advantages of utilizing behavior in groups that rely largely on behavioral rather than structural isolating mechanisms.

Other arthropod groups for which behavior has been correlated with taxonomy include the spiders and crustaceans. Jocelyn Crane's study of the displays of fifteen species of jumping spiders (Salticidae) and nearly fifty species of fiddler crabs (*Uca*, Ocypodidae) has proven the existence of species-typical male displays. In the jumping spiders they may serve as supernumerary isolating mechanisms that supplement other species differences. Among the crabs, in addition to exhibiting species-typical display patterns, there is a correlation between ecology and behavior. Species inhabiting exposed localities tend to have more elaborate male cheliped-waving displays than those living in more sheltered locations.

Patterns of web-spinning by spiders have also been used by taxonomists for judging relationships between higher taxonomic groupings. Thus, affinities have been suggested between the orb-spinning families Argiopidae and Uloboridae. However, others regard this particular case a remarkable example of convergent behavioral evolution. There can be no doubt about the species-specificity of these orb webs; the great English authority on spiders, William Bristowe, concluded that "there are specific, generic and family distinctions in the architecture and construction" of the orb-spinners' webs. He even devised a simple key to the species of orb-spinners he had studied, based on characteristics of the webs spun by adult females. Similarly, a key to the species of the termite genus *Apicotermes* has been published, based on the mode of construction of the subterranean nests, and keys to the species of caddisflies have been devised largely on the characteristics of the cases constructed by the larvae. Recently a key to nearly all the genera of true weaver birds (Ploceinae) was published, based on nest variations. Similar nest keys to species in individual genera, such as *Textor* and *Malimbus*, have also been made.

BEHAVIOR AND HIGHER TAXONOMIC GROUPINGS

As mentioned previously, the "finches" provide a taxonomic problem that is still far from solved, but it appears that behavioral studies are more likely to contribute solutions than are anatomical ones. In Africa several major groups of finches provide an especially interesting example of this problem. One of these groups is comprised of the weaver birds (Ploceinae) just mentioned; the males of which construct fairly elaborate woven nests with lateral or ventral openings. Another group is the large assemblage of waxbills, part of the subfamily Estrildinae. In this group the nest is also often domed and has a lateral entrance, but is not woven. Thirdly, there are the African widow birds (Viduinae), including nine species of social parasites that lay their eggs in the nests of estrildine finches. Because of the remarkable similarity in mouth markings and juvenile plumages of the widow bird young and those of their hosts, it has long been assumed that the Estrildinae and Viduinae are closely related and that both are distinct from the true weavers. However, studies by the German ethologist Jürgen Nicolai have proven, for example, that in courtship behavior, innate song elements, and other behavioral characters the widow birds are definitely more closely related to the true weavers than to their estrildine hosts. Amazingly, the male widow birds learn the entire song vocabulary of their host species through imprinting, and the female widow birds come into reproductive condition only after they have observed breeding behavior among individuals of the host species. The male's song phrases learned from the host species thus serve as an isolating mechanim for the widow birds as well as their hosts! Furthermore, race and species formation in the widow birds and their hosts occur in parallel. No estrildines are parasitized by more than one widow bird; overlapping species of widow birds parasitize different hosts. In some cases the taxonomic relationships of the widow birds can be understood only by studying the relationships of the host species.

In the Northern Hemisphere an almost equally difficult problem revolves around the constitution and taxonomic affinities of two other finchlike groups, the Old World buntings and numerous New World "sparrows" of the subfamily Emberizinae (or Fringillinae), and the more arboreal and social finches (goldfinches, siskins, redpolls) of the Carduelinae. Common taxonomic procedure is to "lump" all these species together in a single large family, the Fringillidae. But some recent taxonomists have favored the recognition of separate families for these groups, and others have suggested that the carduelines should be transferred to a position near the Old World estrildine finches. A comparison of behavior patterns in the two groups provides some evidence on the question. Male cardueline finches usually have a flight song and feed the female during courtship, but these traits are not typical of the emberizines. The cardueline finches usually build their cuplike nests in trees or high bushes in loose colonies; the very similar nests of the more territorial emberizines are normally in low shrubs or on the ground. Carduelines feed their nestlings regurgitated food; the emberizines feed theirs freshly captured insects. Fouling of the nest by accumulation of the older nestlings' feces occurs in nearly all the carduelines, but the emberizines maintain nest sanitation by removing fecal materials. A typical display of male carduelines is to tilt the body away from the female while turning the tail toward her; this display is absent in the emberizines except for one genus (*Fringilla*), which might therefore have to be considered closely related to or part of the cardueline group. These numerous behavioral criteria suggest that the two groups are at least distinct subfamilies, but are probably more closely related to one another than either is to the weavers or waxbills, from which they differ in a number of criteria such as their nest forms and courtship patterns.

The birds of paradise (Paradisaeidae) and bower birds (Ptilinorhynchidae) provide a second example of the use of behavior in distinguishing genera and subfamilies. The typical birds of paradise are believed to be largely polygynous or promiscuous, and the brightly colored males usually display in communal or "exploded" arenas high in the trees. But males of one genus (*Diphyllodes*) display on vertical branches near the ground in cleared display sites, and another genus (*Parotia*) displays on the ground in cleared "dance floors." Additionally, certain genera (*Manucodia* and *Macgregoria*) have monogamous pair bonds, lack plumage dimorphism, and the males assist with nesting duties.

Two subfamilies of bower birds are often recognized. The relatively dull-plumaged catbirds (*Ailuroedus*) are monogamous and the males construct no bower, but rather assist the female in tending the eggs and young. Males of one genus in this subfamily (*Scenopoeetes*) display on the rainforest floor in a cleared circular "stage" that is covered daily with fresh leaves. The other subfamily of bower birds includes species that all construct definite bowers around and in which the males display. The simplest of these is the "mat" bower built by a little-studied genus (*Archboldia*) of New Guinea. Besides clearing a circular stage, a mat of fern fronds is laid down and bordered with various objects, above which a curtain of fern leaves and bamboo is hung. The remaining species can be separated into two groups of genera that are more readily defined behaviorally than morphologically. Two genera are "maypole" builders that center their circular bowers around a central spire, and the other three genera are "avenue" builders, constructing bowers having two or more walls of twigs and branches inserted in the ground. Both groups decorate their bowers with colorful objects such as flowers and leaves, varying with the species. Thus, the bower is species-specific in manner of construction as well as the type and color of objects placed in or around it by the male. Objects of the "wrong" type that are experimentally introduced will be quickly removed by the male. In the satin bower bird the bower is regularly orientated north-south; this orientation appears to be related to an optimum angle relative to the sun from the point where the female usually watches the iridescent male.

These birds provide a number of important lessons relative to behavior and taxonomy. Evolutionary trends in behavior (displays and bower building) and structure (male plumage development) can be traced through both families, and may allow for recognition of "primi-tive" and "advanced" features. However, these words must be used with care; the birds of paradise tend to have highly elaborate ("advanced") male plumages and displays, but lack or have only "primitive" bowers, whereas in bower birds the species building the most "advanced" bowers exhibit relatively simple male plumages. "Primitive" male plumages also occur in the genera of both groups that are monogamous. In both fami-lies, the females are more uniform in appearance than are the males and probably provide a much better index of relationships. In fifteen of the twenty commonly accepted genera of birds of paradise there is strong sexual dimorphism in plumage and very distinctive male plumages, yet in at least ten of these genera the females are very similar to one an-other. Thus, most genera have been based on male plumages, and in both families there is an unrealistically small average number of species per genus (about two). The only large (four species each) genera of bower birds are *Chlamydera* and *Amblyornis,* the males of which con-struct elaborate species-specific bowers and are themselves relatively similar and inconspicuous. Several of the ten or more described species of *Paradisaea* have proven to be only geographic isolates or even hybrids. Wild hybrids between species having remarkably different male plum-ages have been reported, including numerous "intergeneric" crosses. Charles Sibley has therefore suggested that taxonomists have been basing genera on what are really species-specific male characters that are not even fully effective in preventing hybridization under wild conditions.

In spite of the bewildering array of male plumage variations in the birds of paradise, most of the fifteen sexually dimorphic "genera" share common features that are variably developed among these genera. These features include elongation of part or all of the tail or specialization of the two central tail feathers (six genera), long, airy plumes on the lower flanks or colored and erectile pectoral plumes (eight genera), iridescent throat feathers (eleven genera) and iridescent crown feathers and/or erectile napes (thirteen genera). In some species of *Paradisaea* the colorful flank plumes are displayed by being raised and shaken as the bird calls, falls forward, and droops or waves its wings (Fig. 5), and in two others they form a spreading filigree as the male sings while hanging upside down from a branch! In the superb bird of paradise (*Lophorina*) the iridescent throat and elongated cape are erected to form a continuous shield behind the head, the pale greenish gape is opened, and two artificial green "eyes" are exposed above and behind the much less conspicuous real eyes. Similarly, the king bird of paradise

113

(*Cicinnurus*) almost hides its head, but does so by erecting its upper flank feathers as it cocks its tail, so that the two green eyelike spiral tips of its central tail feathers are "juggled" slowly over the head. An equally hypnotic display occurs in the magnificent rifle bird (*Craspedophora*), which spreads its rounded wings like an enormous butterfly and quickly moves its head from side to side so that the flashing green gorget oscillates like an inverted pendulum. And all of these seemingly distinctive genera have been involved in intergeneric hybridization (Fig. 5)!

SPECIES AND INFRASPECIES DIFFERENCES IN BEHAVIOR

If species-specific behavioral characteristics develop during the process of speciation, they must, like structural differences, originate from individual genetic differences produced by mutations and recombinations that gradually accrue in isolated populations. Such isolated populations are likely to diverge gradually in behavior, even in the absence of direct selection for these behavioral differences. For example, there may be pressures favoring behavioral changes as a result of major habitat differences in the isolated populations, as suggested earlier for weaver birds. Or there may be gradual changes in relative agonistic and sexual tendencies which might affect thresholds of display responses. Finally, differential degrees of selection for concealing coloration may affect display conspicuousness. The common mallard and North American black duck are identical in size and display motor patterns, but the dark and somber coloration of the forest-adapted male black duck makes it much less conspicuous than the mallard. On the other hand, black ducks appear to have lower sexual display thresholds than mallards.

Direct selection for behavior changes can also occur in isolated populations if at least one of these populations is in contact with some other related species. Selection for display differences in these two overlapping (*sympatric*) populations would produce behavioral differences between the isolated (*allopatric*) populations of the original species. This source of selection may explain why the Pacific eider (*Somateria mollissima v. nigra*), which is sympatric with three other eider species, differs so much in its behavior from the European eider (*S. m. mollissima*), which

Fig. 5. Male Displays of Twelve-wired Bird of Paradise (A), Lesser Bird of Paradise (B), King Bird of Paradise (C), Rifle Bird (D), Superb Bird of Paradise (E) and Magnificent Bird of Paradise (F). Lines indicate reported hybrid combinations.

A

B

C

D

E

F

C.G.Pritchard

is only partially sympatric with one other eider. Secondly, there may be an enhanced rate of behavioral divergence between populations as a result of selection for reducing competition or maintaining isolation after the reestablishment of limited contact between previously isolated populations. In such cases behavior and/or structural differences in the zone of sympatry are typically greater than those present in the areas of allopatry. Examples of such reinforcement of species differences (or *character divergence*) have been found in numerous groups, ranging from grasshoppers (*Chorthippus brunneus* and *C. biguttulus*), to frogs (species of *Microhyla* and *Acris*) and birds (rock nuthatches of the genus *Sitta*). On the other hand, relaxation of pressures for species-specificity in forms normally sympatric with other related species may occur in completely isolated populations, as on islands. It is known that in birds there may be a resulting secondary loss of behavioral species-specificity, either in visual displays (island races of various ducks) or vocalizations (island forms of songbirds).

If these ideas are correct, it should be possible to demonstrate varying degrees of intraspecific variations in behavior, including both individual variation and geographic racial variation. Individual behavioral variants frequently occur among captive male ducks, which may perform a display atypical of the species but found in related species, or which perform a species-typical display in an aberrant manner. Geographic variation in vocalizations has been demonstrated in the songs of a large number of bird species and also in the calls of various frogs and toads.

The studies of Frank McKinney on two races of the common eider provide an excellent example of geographic variation in behavior. In studying thirteen male displays, he found that ten occur in both races, eight have the same form in both races, six occur in the same situations in both races, and only one occurs at the same estimated frequency in both races. Additionally, two displays occur at slightly different frequencies, seven at markedly different frequencies, three are completely absent in some situations, two take a distinctly different form in the two races, and three are completely absent in one race. Similarly, various accounts of the male displays of the blue grouse (*Dendragapus obscurus*) indicate that the coastal populations ("sooty" grouse) differ from the interior populations ("dusky" grouse) in several aspects. The dense-forest-dwelling coastal birds usually display in a solitary and highly territorial fashion, uttering loud and resonant calls from trees. The air sacs exposed during this calling are yellow. The interior races occupy more open forests, and males normally display on the ground, have weaker calls, and reddish air sacs. The "flash effect" of the wide white feather border around the pulsating air sacs can be seen for considerable distance in this open country, thus possibly compensating for the weaker calls.

In summary, it would appear that quantitative (frequency and situation) differences in behavior are the first to appear in isolated populations, perhaps as a result of response threshold differences caused by "tendency" changes. These may increase as a result of direct or indirect selection pressures, and may eventually result in major qualitative behavioral differences between populations.

When the proper precautions of interpretation are taken, behavior may thus serve as a valuable adjunct to morphological studies. Frequently it serves to bolster morphologically based conclusions; for example, a close correlation between morphological and behavioral classifications of the eleven species of the *Drosophila obscura* group has been found. Likewise, in the waterfowl family Anatidae behavioral evidence has helped to resolve the systematic status of several morphologically specialized or otherwise "aberrant" species. Behavior is of particular value in recognizing sibling species that rely largely or entirely on behavioral isolating mechanisms; indeed, in some instances it provides the most practical method of taxonomic discrimination. Behavioral discrimination has thus proved useful for a number of insects such as crickets (stridulation patterns), fireflies (flashing patterns) and Lepidoptera (identification of larval host plants). This slowly widening recognition of the systematic significance of behavior, first fully appreciated by many leading avian taxonomists, has led Howard Evans to predict cautiously that the time may not be too far away when taxonomists in general will "become students of animals instead of students of corpses and skeletons."

SUGGESTED READING

ALEXANDER, R. D., "The Role of Behavioral Study in Cricket Classification." *Systematic Zoology* 11:53-72, 1962.

BLAIR, W. F., "Non-Morphological Data in Anuran Classification." *Systematic Zoology* 11:72-84, 1962.

CARPENTER, C. C., "A Comparison of the Patterns of Display of *Urosaurus. Uta* and *Streptosaurus.*" *Herpetologica* 18:145-152, 1962.

CROOK, J. H., "Comparative Studies on the Reproductive Behavior of Two Closely Related Weaver Bird Species (*Ploceus cucullatus* and *Ploceus nigerrimus*) and Their Races." *Behaviour* 21: 177-232, 1963.

FICKEN, R. W., and FICKEN, M. S., "A Review of Some Aspects of Avian Field Ethology." *Auk* 83:637-661, 1966.

HINDE, R. A., and TINBERGEN, N., "The Comparative Study of Species-Specific Behavior." In ROE, A., and SIMPSON, G. G. (eds.), *Behavior and Evolution.* New Haven, Conn.: Yale University Press, 1958, pp. 251-268.

JOHNSGARD, P. A., *Handbook of Waterfowl Behavior.* Ithaca, N. Y.: Cornell University Press, 1965, 378 pp.

MAYR, ERNST, "Behavior and Systematics." In ROE, A., and SIMPSON, G. G. eds.), *Behavior and Evolution.* New Haven, Conn.: Yale University Press, 1958, 557 pp.

——, "Birds of Paradise." *Natural History* 54: 264-276, 1945.

McKINNEY, FRANK, "An Analysis of the Displays of the European Eider *Somateria mollissima mollissima* (Linnaeus) and the Pacific Eider *Somateria mollissima v. nigra* Bonaparte." *Behaviour,* Supplement VII, 1961, 124 pp.

SIBLEY, C. G., "The Evolutionary and Taxonomic Significance of Sexual Dimorphism and Hybridization in Birds." *Condor* 50:166-191, 1957

TINBERGEN, N., "The Evolution of Behavior in Gulls." *Scientific American,* December, 1960, pp. 118-130. (Available in offprint form.)

CHAPTER 11

Behavioral evolution and speciation

As is now well known, evolution in organisms depends upon genetic variation and natural selection, and, in addition, prolonged geographic isolation is probably crucial for achieving speciation in sexually reproducing animals. It was shown in Chapter 8 that behavior is regulated by genes; we might now consider the effects of selection, evolution, and geographic isolation on behavior.

It is difficult to prove that measurable behavioral changes may be produced by natural selection, which usually operates at levels too low for its effects to be easily detected in a reasonable length of time. But as indicated earlier, it is often possible to produce major behavioral differences in only a few generations through intense artificial selection. In *Drosophila melanogaster*, lines have been selected for positive and negative phototaxis, producing almost complete behavioral separation in less than thirty generations. Similarly, separation of positive and negatively geotactic lines has been achieved within twenty generations. More significantly, by selecting for fast and slow mating speeds a marked separation has been obtained in only seven generations when average mating speeds of eighty *vs.* three minutes were observed. Offspring from crosses between these lines exhibited speeds intermediate between those of the parentals, which apparently thus differ in sexual response thresholds. From such experimental results we must conclude that behavior is highly susceptible to changes through the pressures of selection.

BEHAVIORAL PHYLOGENIES

If behavior, like structure, evolves as species and groups evolve, then it must be imagined that phylogenies of behavior as well as phylogenies of structure develop through time. Unlike many structures, behavior leaves no direct fossils, excluding such remains as fossil tracks and burrows. However, evolution proceeds at different rates in different organ systems and organisms. Therefore, it is often possible to find within animal groups certain species which exhibit more generalized (or "primitive") conditions of structure and behavior than exist in others. By studying such species and comparing them with related forms that are more specialized in these regards, it is sometimes possible to deduce evolutionary trends in behavior as they are expressed in contemporaneous related species. There are several dangers in this practice, such as deciding which way to "read" such a behavioral series, and avoiding confusion of a highly advanced but seemingly simple trait with a "primitive" one. Further, the recognition and utilization of homologous rather than analogous features for comparison is mandatory. Thus, it is assumed that the "maypole" and "avenue" types of bowers evolved from simpler forms such as the "stage" and "mat" types that are still constructed by a few bower birds, and that the latter are not degenerate or independently evolved types.

Such studies of evolutionary trends in behavior, or *ethoclines,* have been made for various groups that contain species having extraordinarily complex behavior patterns. The evolution of these patterns can sometimes be understood through the study of related species having more generalized characters. For example, during the courtship of the carnivorous "balloon flies" of the family Empididae, the males of several species fly about in the sky carrying silken balloons as large as or larger than themselves, and which serve to attract females. It is difficult without comparative studies to visualize how such an unlikely display evolved. When such studies were undertaken a number of behavioral variations were found in related species, which can be organized into a series of increasing complexity. In many species, including the genus *Tachydromia,* the male lacks any obvious displays and attempts to mate directly with the female, who often attacks him. In *Empimorpha comata* the male brings the female a prey specimen which she eats during mating. In certain species of *Hilara* a few strands of silken thread, presumably from the anal gland, are wrapped around the prey to subdue it. In *Empis* species the male completely wraps the prey in thread, thus forming a small balloon. In *Empimorpha geneatis* the balloon is relatively large, although the prey is fairly small and may already have been sucked dry by the male. Finally, in *Hilara sartor* the large and conspicuous balloon may contain nothing edible at all!

Equally interesting evolutionary trends in behavior have been described by Howard Evans for various groups of wasps. These trends can be observed on a broad scale through the solitary and social wasps, as well as on a more restricted scale within certain families such as the solitary spider wasps (Pompilidae) or the social wasps (Vespidae). Evidently the earliest wasps were strictly vegetarians, as is still the case with males. These early wasps, now represented by such forms as sawflies, deposited their eggs in plant tissues and were usually highly host-specific, since the larvae fed on the plant materials. Next, the "parasitoid" wasps developed, including such now-existing groups as the ichneumon flies whose females deposited their eggs on or in another arthropod, usually a plant forager. In these forms, the larvae fed on the host animal's tissues, causing its death.

The more modern "predatoid" wasps inherited this general behavior from their ancestors, but they paralyze their prey by stinging them. They then usually transport them to a nest and store them in this helpless state to await the hatching of the eggs. Some of these predatoid wasps are highly host specific, whereas others are less so. The spider-hunting pompilid wasps such as the tarantula hawk *Pepsis* are an example of the least advanced predatoid wasps, the females of which usually catch their prey before they build their nests or lay eggs. Typically the prey is larger than the wasp, and only one individual is used. The nest is built near the place where the prey is found, and after being stung it is dragged to the nest by the wasp. The egg is then laid and the nest is closed.

An intermediate stage of development is exhibited by such digger wasps as the Sphecidae, which include the sand wasps *Ammophila* and *Philanthus* mentioned earlier. These forms usually build their nests before they capture their prey consisting of spiders, orthopteran insects, or lepidopterous larvae. The more generalized members of the family limit their prey to spiders and relatively primitive insects, whereas the more advanced subfamilies prey largely on the larvae or adults of holometabolous insects. In these advanced forms the prey is often smaller than the wasp and may be taken at some distance from the nest. It is carried in flight by the female wasp, who may hold it in her mandible, carry it with her middle legs, or, in the most advanced forms, hold it on specialized segments of the abdomen or sting.

The vespoid wasps include a number of advanced solitary species as well as the social wasps. The solitary forms such as *Odynerus* may excavate earthen nests similar to those of the digger wasps or may construct elegant mud nests, as seen in the potter wasps (*Eumenes*). In both of these genera the egg is suspended from the roof above the paralyzed prey, and is thus safe from crushing should the paralysis wear off. In some related forms (*Zethus*), a simple nest is made of leaf fragments stuck together, forming one or more cells. Progressive rather than mass provisioning occurs in several solitary wasps, and in at least certain species of *Zethus* direct feeding of recently captured prey to the larvae is performed by the female, providing the most important step toward the development of prolonged interdependency between generations and thus establishing a primitive social system. In the truly social wasps a more elaborate nest is made, containing combs constructed of masticated plant materials. The smaller colonies having only a single fertile female ("queen") may have only a single comb (*Polistes, Stenogaster*), or several horizontal combs arranged in vertical series and surrounded by a paper envelope (*Vespa*). In the large polygynous colonies having numerous fertile females, the number of comb layers is often fairly large, and the paper-like envelope may be incomplete (*Protopolybia*) or it may completely enclose the combs and have only a small ventral opening (*Nectarina*). In contrast to the bees. which developed from different ancestors related to the modern Specidae, even these advanced forms have retained an "upside-down" comb with the opening facing downward, presumably a now functionless holdover from the time when the eggs were safely suspended above the paralyzed food supply. The social bees probably evolved in much the same manner as the social wasps, by the association of females and their young through prolonged maternal contact, or by the communal nesting of several females of the same generation.

The remaining social hymenopterans, the ants, clearly evolved from vespoidlike stock. The most generalized of these, the Ponerinae, are definitely wasplike and have carnivorous behavior, painful stings, and relatively little caste dimorphism between queens and workers. The somewhat more advanced army ants (Dorylinae) are also predacious, but live in larger colonies and are nomadic. The remaining subfamilies of ants show increasing tendencies toward large colonies with caste polymorphism, vegetarian food habits, rudimentary stings, and complex behavior patterns related to their foraging requirements. These trends culminate in the almost unbelievable social organization and food-getting behavior of the dairy ants that tend "herds" of aphids, the leaf-cutting ants that grow fungus "gardens," and the "slave-maker" ants that steal and rear the eggs and young of other ants to serve as captive workers.

One last example of behavioral phylogeny may be mentioned; the evolution of spider webs. Although all spiders produce silk, not all make webs. Rather, the original function of spider silk may have been to cover the eggs, as is found in the more primitive arachnids such as whip-scorpions and pseudoscorpions. The use of silk for other purposes, such as ballooning and as snares, was presumably a secondary development. Various people have proposed theories to account for the origin of webs and other snares, as outlined recently by Benjamin Kaston. Most probably, simple snares were first produced by chance, as silk lines were laid down around retreats or attached to vegetation to support egg sacs. It is possible that the "maze" or "scaffolding" type of snare, as found in the Theridiidae and Pholcidae thus developed around an egg sac suspended from vegetation. From this irregular meshwork of fibers the more organized "sheet" webs may have arisen, on which the spider clings upside down. The eggs may be attached to the undersurface of this sheet or placed in an adjacent chamber. A separate trend developed in the more terrestrial spiders, which hide the eggs in holes, or in enclosed silken cells. By the laying down of draglines from such a retreat, a primitive snare or alerting system may have been initiated, which later could have been elaborated into sheet webs with a funnel entrance, as in the Agelenidae. Unlike the Pholcidae, with similar webs, the spider runs on the upper surface of the sheet.

An increase in snaring efficiency, combined with a reduction of silk required, was eventually achieved by the development of viscid threads. This much more effective catching method is associated with the complex and beautiful orb webs of the families Argiopidae and Uloboridae. Possibly the orb web of the Argiopidae evolved from a maze web to which a viscid spiral was added. In the typical orb weavers the viscid spiral is laid down after the supporting frame and radii are in place, and also after a nonviscid provisional or scaffold spiral has been laid down. However, some genera form only the provisional spiral on their maze of nonviscid threads. More typically, the orb weavers remove the provisional spiral as they lay down the viscid spiral, and do not build a surrounding maze. Evidently the orb-web of *Uloborus*, which is made in a very similar manner, evolved from a different ancestral web type which was tubular, with orblike supports.

In a genus related to *Uloborus*, a much simpler web is produced that resembles the triangular sector of an orb and is crossed by viscid lines corresponding to the spiral of an orb web. The apex of the triangle is attached to a twig by a single line, which the spider severs and holds in her legs, keeping the net taut. When an insect strikes the web, she releases the thread, springing the trap. A more remarkable snare is produced by species of a related family (Dinopidae), which builds a somewhat rectangular web crossed with viscid bands. This net is held in an expanded state by the spider's front legs, and is actually dropped or thrown over its prey! An equally incredible adaptation is found in the bolas spiders of America, South Africa, and Australia. These remarkable spiders do not spin any webs at all, but hold lines of silk tipped with sticky globules that are thrown at passing insects. In the South African species the line is not thrown but whirled about horizontally bolas-fashion as the spider waits for its prey to fly into the trap! Willis Gertsch has thoroughly described and illustrated the amazing behavioral adaptations of these spiders.

These examples of ethoclines help point out the fact that when we are faced with behavior patterns that boggle the imagination, such as birds that build and decorate elaborate bowers, bees that "dance," and spiders that lasso their prey, it is often possible to gain an understanding of the probable evolution of these remarkable behaviors through comparative studies of related species.

BEHAVIOR AND SPECIATION

A process related to the evolutionary change in structure and behavior through time is that of speciation, or the multiplication of species. It is now generally held that geographic isolation is required for this process to occur, at least in the groups considered here. As is also believed to be true of morphology, behavioral differences in isolated populations probably accrue gradually as a result of genetic variation and natural selection. Some of the direct and indirect sources of selection for behavioral divergence were mentioned in the preceding chapter. Divergence in three behavioral aspects are believed particularly significant in the consideration of speciation, those patterns concerned with *mate selection, food selection,* and *habitat selection.* The ecological aspects of behavior concerned with foraging adaptations and habitat adaptations that might reduce interspecific competition have been mentioned previously, and so particular attention will be paid here to the evolution of behavioral adaptations concerned with mate selection.

The writings of Robert Hinde and Niko Tinbergen, who have formulated most of the arguments having a bearing on the evolution and significance of interspecific differences in mate selection, are of particular importance and will be utilized here. Direct evidence indicating the efficiency of interspecific differences in mate selection is provided by the rarity of hybrids in nature, even between species which produce fully fertile hybrids such as many ducks. Indirect evidence of the importance of interspecific differences in mate selection behavior can be shown in a number of ways. For example, the fact that early pair-forming displays in waterfowl tend to be more elaborate and species-specific than later pair-maintaining displays indicates that the prevention of mixed pairing was a major factor in the evolution of elaborate pair-forming displays. Secondly, character divergence (or "displacement") in behavioral patterns associated with reproductive isolation sometimes occurs in the zone of sympatry between closely related but largely allopatric species. Finally, since the responsibility for mate selection (and species recognition) usually resides in the female sex, it is typical that males exhibit the more elaborate displays and show less discrimination toward females, whereas females usually have more inconspicuous displays but exhibit discrimination against any males that do not possess species-typical behavior or appearance. Sexual selection also affects this last point, and may result in marked sexual dimorphism of behavior and structure even in the absence of selection for reproductive isolation.

It has already been mentioned that the first steps toward behavioral differences in isolated populations are quantitative ones, perhaps producing changes in response thresholds. These quantitative variations may be developed in at least three ways, according to Robert Hinde. The first involves the development of differences in *relative and actual motivational tendencies* (attack, escape, sex) of one sex toward the other. This trend may bring about changes in the thresholds of sexual and agonistic responses during pair formation or other sexual encounters. Secondly, differences in the *degree of sexual dimorphism in behavior* may develop, particularly if changes occur in structural sexual dimorphism. In general, as females come to look more and more distinct from males, males tend initially to respond less aggressively and instead exhibit stronger sexual responses. Thirdly, there may develop differences in *signaling motor patterns* by one or both sexes, but particularly the "courting" sex. These are basically the result of changes in the degrees of ritualization of various equivalent motor patterns in the two populations. The more a motor pattern becomes ritualized for signal purposes, the more it is "emancipated" from its original physiological function, although sometimes the unritualized precursor persists along with the ritualized version. In many cases, both the signaling behavior and the signaling device (feathers, hair, skin, etc.) are ritualized simultaneously; in this way structural and behavioral differences between populations may be promoted and may later possibly serve as a basis for isolating mechanisms.

In these manners, interpopulation and interspecific differences in displays may gradually develop. These may include differences in *frequencies* or *intensities* at which a display is performed, reflecting the differences in motivations or threshold-response levels mentioned above, or producing changes in "typical intensity" of display performance. There may be differences in the *coordination* or *linkage* of display components, producing different sequences of postures, movements, or sounds. More than a dozen related ducks of the genus *Anas* perform several homologous displays including the "head-up-tail-up," "grunt-whistle," and "down-up," but in different species these are performed with varying degrees of linkage and sequential arrangement, as well as by differences in motor coordination, plumage patterns displayed, and associated vocalizations. An extension of frequency differences is the possibility of a complete *loss of certain displays* in one species, while another may "specialize" in that particular display. For example, male South American pintails (*Anas spinicauda*) repeatedly perform the grunt-whistle but never the head-up-tail-up or down-up, but those of the closely related Bahama pintail (*Anas bahamensis*) lack the grunt-whistle and have a uniquely fused down-up — head-up-tail-up combination. Displays in related species may vary in *speed of performance* or *frequency of repetition*. These variations are often associated with body size; smaller species usually perform homologous displays faster than do larger relatives. Thus, in the precopulatory situation the male common eider performs between ten and twenty displays per minute, but the smaller Steller's eider (*Polysticta stelleri*) performs between thirty and sixty per minute. The development of *rhythmic repetition* in displays may vary between species. The "pushing" display as performed by king eiders (*Somateria spectabilis*) is nearly always done three or four times in rapid succession, but the corresponding display in the spectacled eider (*S. fischeri*) is performed singly. Finally, differences in *orientation* may develop in related species. Some species of ducks regularly perform certain displays such as the head-up-tail-up at profile view to the female, but this orientation is weak or lacking in others.

In summary, it may be seen that behavioral characteristics evolve as species evolve, and that behavioral adaptations are subject to divergent, convergent, or parallel evolution in exactly the same manner as structural characters. In particular, behavioral differences at the species level are extremely important in that they might serve to reduce interspecific competition for food or habitat, or may protect the species from disadvantageous hybridization. This latter function of behavioral differences, providing reproductive isolation, will be considered more thoroughly in the next chapter.

SUGGESTED READING

EMERSON, A. E., "The Evolution of Behavior Among Social Insects." In ROE, A. and SIMPSON, G. G. (eds.), *Behavior and Evolution.* New Haven, Conn.: Yale University Press, 1958, pp. 311-335.

EVANS, HOWARD, "Predatory Wasps," *Scientific American,* April, 1963, pp. 144-154.

———, *Comparative Ethology and Evolution of the Sand Wasps.* Cambridge, Mass.: Harvard University Press, 1966. 576 pp.

GERTSCH, W. J., "Spiders That Lasso Their Prey," *Natural History* 56: 152-159, April, 1947. (See also *Bulletin of the American Museum of Natural History* 106:227-254, 1955.)

HINDE, R. A., "Behaviour and Speciation in Birds and Lower Vertebrates." *Biological Reviews* 34:85-128, 1959.

KASTON, B. J., "The Evolution of Spider Webs." *American Zoologist* 4:191-207, 1964. (See also *Natural History* 66:26-32, April, 1966.)

ROE, ANNE, and SIMPSON, G. G. (eds.), *Behavior and Evolution.* New Haven, Conn.: Yale University Press, 1958, 557 pp.

TINBERGEN, N., "The Evolution of Signaling Devices." In ETKIN, WILLIAM (ed.), *Social Behavior and Organization Among Vertebrates.* Chicago: University of Chicago Press, 1964, pp. 206-230.

CHAPTER 12

Behavioral isolating mechanisms

It has been asserted that an environment-imposed (*extrinsic*) isolation of some form, most probably geographic, is indispensible for the initial stages of speciation, during which isolated populations diverge genetically. With the progression of speciation in two such populations to a point when they are *reproductively isolated,* we may say that *intrinsic isolating mechanisms* have been established and will thereafter serve to keep the populations' gene pools apart even if the extrinsic factors should be disrupted. Therefore, all species reproducing sexually and sympatrically must possess intrinsic isolating mechanisms that prevent them from a significant amount of interbreeding. These mechanisms may be classified into the following general categories, based partly on arrangements proposed by Ernst Mayr and John Mecham:

I. Premating mechanisms (functioning prior to gamete release)

   A. The species do not meet during reproduction
     1. The species reproduce at different times (*temporal isolation*)
     2. The species are ecologically segregated during reproduction (*ecological isolation*)

   B. The species meet but gametes are not released
     1. Behavioral differences prevent gamete release (*ethological isolation*)
     2. Copulation is prevented by size or structural differences (*mechanical isolation*)

II. Postmating mechanisms (functioning after gamete release)
   A. Gametes are released but hybrids are not produced
      1. Gametic mortality prevents zygote formation (*gametic isolation*)
      2. Zygotic or embryonic mortality resulting from major genetic differences prevents hybrid production (*genic isolation*)
   B. Hybrids are produced but are unsuccessful (incomplete genic isolation)
      1. Hybrids are of reduced vitality and die prematurely (*hybrid inviability*)
      2. Hybrids are sterile or of reduced fertility (*hybrid sterility*)
      3. Hybrids are fertile but are unable to obtain mates, or cannot compete with parentals for niche requirements (*hybrid adaptive inferiority*)

Reproductive isolation can thus occur at almost any stage of the reproductive cycle, well prior to fertilization or at a much later time. Clearly, it would be to a species' benefit that isolation occur prior to gamete release so that reproductive efficiency of the species is highest, and gamete wastage is avoided. Therefore, it might be expected that natural selection would favor the replacement of postmating isolating mechanisms by more efficient premating mechanisms operating in time to avoid or correct possible "mistakes." In the invertebrates and lower vertebrates it appears that seasonal isolation is an important premating mechanism, particularly in aquatic animals or others living in an environment where favorable periods for reproduction can be readily timed by some reliable external factor. Thus, seasonal differences in reproduction may play a role in the isolation of such vertebrates as frogs, which are known to have widely staggered periods of reproduction in temperate regions. Shorter temporal variations in breeding behavior, such as diel activity patterns, are also believed to be significant in such frog genera as *Microhyla*. Seasonal reproduction is probably an important factor in insects, as suggested by the sequential breeding periods of sympatric species in various groups. Furthermore, ecological isolation may be of somewhat greater significance in small invertebrates than in larger and highly mobile animals, whose ecology may not be so closely adapted to such "microniches" as total dependence on a particular host plant, prey species, or substrate.

Excluding the possibilities of temporal and ecological isolation, which may themselves have behavioral bases, we are left with ethological isolation as a primary premating isolating mechanism, since mechanical isolation is now believed to be of minor importance even in insects. Doubtlessly, behavioral isolation is most feasible in those species utilizing internal fertilization, or which at least depend upon direct stimulation by the opposite sex for the release of gametes. In these species there is generally a smaller number of gametes required to achieve fertilization, as well as taxon-specific behavior patterns associated with reproduction. These groups include animals having internal fertilization via copulation (mammals, birds, reptiles, various fish, and most terrestrial arthropods), those directly passing sperm or spermatophores to females in water (crustaceans, cephalopods, urodele amphibians) or on land (spiders, onychophorans), and those simultaneously expelling gametes in the water by individual stimulation (many fish, anuran amphibians, and marine polychaetes).

Once individual fertilization through mutual stimulation is achieved, the likelihood of behavioral isolating mechanisms replacing postmating ones is greatly increased. Furthermore, the longer the period between the initial attraction of the sexes and the time of fertilization, the greater is the potential for behavioral isolating mechanisms effectively preventing fertilizations between species.

The timing and means of the initial attraction between the sexes thus becomes an important factor in isolation. The males may be attracted to and seek out females at a certain time, based on the latter's signaling behavior (odors, sounds, visual displays) when reproductively active. Alternatively, the females may be attracted by the activity of sexually mature males. These males may gather in social courting units (mobile groups or in fixed arenas) and attract the females by their joint activity, or they may perform individually in larger territories and repel other males. In either case, a male might fertilize only a single female or several, although the latter is more probable in communal display areas. In such polygamous or promiscuous species the female-attracting behavior may replace elaborate precopulatory behavior, and is usually therefore species-specific. When there is a longer period between initial social attraction and fertilization, immediately effective isolating mechanisms are not so critical. In such species behavioral isolation might occur at the time of the social group's formation, at the time of pair (or harem) formation, or at some later time prior to gamete release.

The means of achieving behavioral isolation is thus greatly varied in different animals but is basically dependent upon signaling behavior between the sexes which results in "species recognition." It can therefore be expected that behavioral isolating mechanisms might take the form of any of the signaling methods mentioned earlier, including visual, acoustical, chemical, tactile, or even electrical types. Much has been learned about visual and acoustical isolating mechanisms in recent years, but little is known about chemical and tactile isolating mechanisms. Nothing is known about possible electrical isolating mechanisms, although species-specific electrical impulses are known to occur in some fish. Some specific examples of chemical, acoustical, and visual isolating mechanisms may now be considered.

CHEMICAL ISOLATING MECHANISMS

Olfactory signaling behavior is unquestionably of great significance as an isolating mechanism in certain groups of animals. The sensitivity of male mammals to the scent of sexually active females is well known to the owner of female dogs or cats; estrus females are able to attract males from surprising distances. The olfactory attraction of newly emerged female moths to males of its species is even more remarkable; female cecropia (*Samia*) and promethea (*Callosamia*) moths are said to be capable of attracting males from a distance of several miles! It has been reported that freshly emerged female European tiger moths (*Panaxia dominula*) of an Italian subspecies are not so effective in attracting males of the Swiss subspecies as are females of that geographic race, suggesting that there may be geographic variation in olfactory isolating mechanisms. Olfactory isolation also appears to play a role in maintaining separation of certain sibling *Drosophila* species, such as between *D. affinis* and *D. algonquin*, and also between *D. willistoni* and *D. capricorni*.

In their book on animal communication, Herbert and Mable Frings report that male hunting spiders can recognize the draglines laid down by others of their species, through chemoreceptors on the legs. In water, chemical signals are also of importance. Thus, males of a polychaete worm (*Grubea clavata*) release with their sperm a material into the water that stimulates ovulation by females; moreover, the ova contain a stimulant for additional sperm release by males. This mutual sexual stimulation material is specific to the genus and may be species-specific. Similarly, female salamanders release into the water sex attractants that are probably species-specific, thus explaining why male court-ship patterns in related sympatric species may be nearly identical. Chemical secretions by males that stimulate female courtship possibly also are present, and probably supplement tactile and visual stimuli provided by the male.

ACOUSTIC ISOLATING MECHANISMS

Acoustic isolating mechanisms have been especially well studied in three groups of animals: the sound-producing insects, anuran amphibians, and birds. Thus, a large number of examples of acoustical isolation could be cited that indicate the importance of this method of maintaining reproductive isolation in these animal groups.

In a study of two sibling species of grasshoppers, *Chortippus brunneus* and *C. biguttulus,* acoustical differences in the male stridulation patterns are the only barrier to hybridization. When the species are experimentally hybridized, the resulting offspring are fertile but unable to attract females, presumably because of their intermediate signaling behavior. Several other cases of acoustical isolation have been studied in various crickets and cicadas. As in the grasshoppers mentioned, these mechanisms are dependent upon proper discrimination by the females which are attracted to the species-typical stridulation patterns of the males. In some Orthoptera such as certain grasshoppers the female may also produce noises, allowing for more efficient signaling. Some insects produce weak sounds that may be readily overlooked by humans but are of significance nonetheless. For example, during courtship the males of the sibling *Drosophila* species *D. persimilis* and *D. pseudoobscura* produce pulsed vibration sounds that differ considerably and probably contribute to reproductive isolation in these sympatric species.

Behavioral isolation in closely related frogs and toads is probably dependent primarily upon auditory differences and secondarily on tactile signals. Different species utilize different methods of amplexus, ranging from pelvic to cephalic, and, in addition, relative skin rugosity may provide supplementary tactile stimulation, at least in toads. Ecological and temporal differences in breeding may replace acoustical isolation in some sympatric species, but the importance of call differences has been proven for several. For example, each of fourteen anuran species has been found to differ from all the others of the same area in at least two of three acoustical variables studied (frequency, trill rate and duration of call). In closely related species which are partially sympatric the calls of the two forms sometimes differ more in the areas of overlap than in regions of allopatry. This divergence has been shown in such related species pairs as tree frogs (*Microhyla carolinensis* and *M. olivacea*), cricket frogs (*Acris gryllus* and *A. crepitans*) and toads (*Bufo americana* and *B. fowleri*).

Species-specific acoustical signals that could serve as isolating mechanisms are certainly widespread in birds, as suggested by the fact that many naturalists can identify all the local songbird species by their primary songs alone. The isolating function of vocalizations has been proven in such sympatric sibling species as the eastern and western meadowlarks (*Sturnella magna* and *S. neglecta*). Robert Stein has gathered evidence that the alder flycatcher (*Empidonax traillii*) is actually comprised of two sympatric species easily recognized by song type and thus reproductively isolated, but which are morphologically nearly identical. Some ecological differences also exist, but little if any seasonal isolation is present. No conclusive evidence indicating hybridization has been found, and there is some indication of structural and behavioral character divergence in the western populations having prolonged sympatry.

VISUAL ISOLATING MECHANISMS

Visual isolating mechanisms are, of course, best developed in diurnal animals having good eyesight and in nocturnal species utilizing luminous signals. Furthermore, animals having color vision (birds, reptiles, fish, and insects) are likely to utilize color patterns as important aspects of their visual isolating mechanisms. Species-typical male displays that may partially serve as isolating mechanisms have also been described in such "lower" arthropods as fiddler crabs (*Uca*) and jumping spiders (Salticidae), and the numerous and colorful patterns assumed by various cephalopods during spermatophore transfer may possibly function in reproductive isolation as well as provide indicators of internal "motivation." Many of the deep-sea cephalopods have species-specific luminous patterns, as do fishes of the same zones. However, it is in the insects and birds that the finest examples of visual isolating mechanisms are to be found.

The flash patterns of North American fireflies of the genus *Photuris* provide an example of species-specific signaling behavior that undoubtedly is an important basis for reproductive isolation in this group. Studies by H. S. Barber indicate species-typical variation in flashing intensity, intervals (less than one second to over seven seconds), color of flashes (yellowish or orange to greenish or blue-green), duration of individual flashes (up to two seconds or more), and other features allowing for ready visual recognition in each of the types.

In comparing the courtship behavior of over 100 species of *Drosophila*, Herman Spieth found that there are important interspecific differences in the positions and movements of males prior to copulation. The majority of the species studied take a courting position behind the female, apparently the "primitive" method. But some species take positions behind or beside the female, and a few orient in front of her. There are also important species differences in the actions of the males, involving proboscis movements, leg movements, and wing movements prior to copulation. Males of most species lick the female continuously, but others do so intermittently. Males of most species rub the female's abdomen with the legs (the abdominal area varies in diferent species); others tap her abdomen. Finally, the wing movements differ in angle in various species and consist of vibration (in most), flicking, waving, or combinations of these. Very closely related species evidently have identical visual mating patterns, but probably reinforce their visual displays with specific olfactory or auditory stimuli.

Visual isolating mechanisms in birds are especially important for those groups lacking elaborate vocalizations, those tending toward polygamy or promiscuity, and those including a number of closely related sympatric species not otherwise reproductively isolated. The gulls (Laridae) have few vocalizations, but are strongly monogamous and rarely exhibit extensive sympatry between closely related species. One place where sympatry does occur and has been well studied by Neal Smith is in northeastern Canada, where the herring gull (*Larus argentatus*) is locally sympatric with the Thayer's gull (*L. thayeri*) and Kumlien's gull (*L. glaucoides kumlieni*); the last two are also locally sympatric with one another. The herring gull has a darker mantle than the others, but mantle color is evidently not a significant isolating mechanism. It also has yellow orbital skin and light iris coloration, unlike the darker purplish orbital colors of the other sympatric species, and this difference appears to be crucial in maintaining reproductive isolation, at least during early stages of pair formation. The color of the orbital skin and iris of the Thayer's gull is dark throughout its range, but where Thayer's gull and the very similar Kumlien's gull come into contact in the northern part of the latter's range, the orbital color of Kumlien's gull is light and distinct from that of Thayer's gull. Females of the two species are more sensitive to orbital color in the region of sympatry than in areas of allopatry. By painting the orbital area of one species the color of the other, Dr. Smith found that males would no longer mount females, and not only were conspecific pairs disrupted, but also mixed pairing was induced.

The grebes (Podicipedidae) are somewhat similar to the gulls in their pair-bond behavior, in that the monogamous condition is strong. All the grebes exhibit only slight sexual dimorphism in size and head plumes, and both sexes alternate between a dull winter plumage and a variably brighter nuptial plumage. Many grebe "courtship" displays are thus presumably concerned with pair-maintenance, and are typically performed mutually by both sexes (Fig. 3). Moreover, displays concerned with pair formation and maintenance are more species-specific than those associated with copulation. The behavior of most of the North American grebes has been studied by Robert Storer, who found that there is a direct correlation between the presence of congeneric sympatric species and the degree of crest or plumage development, and an inverse correlation between the relative development of vocalizations vs. visual displays and plumage features. Dr. Storer has also suggested that the species-typical differences present in the "discovery ceremony," advertising calls, and head plumage patterns between species provide important isolating mechanisms in the relatively large genus *Podiceps* (which includes the eared, horned and red-necked grebes).

The grouse provide a final comparison of behavioral isolating mechanisms. In contrast to the grebes and gulls, at least several species are promiscuous and males defend small territories in common display grounds, or leks, where they display to the females attracted there for copulation. These typical lek-forming species include prairie chickens, sharp-tailed grouse, and sage grouse. The blue grouse (*Dendragapus obscurus*) defends much larger and more permanent territories in "exploded" leks and may perhaps be considered polygamous rather than promiscuous. It thus appears to be somewhat intermediate between the completely promiscuous lek species and the normally monogamous ptarmigans (*Lagopus* spp.). The status of the probably polygamous ruffed grouse (*Bonasa umbellus*) and the possibly monogamous spruce grouse (*Canachites canadensis*) is still disputed, but both species are highly territorial and do not display socially. The two prairie-dwelling species of grouse, the prairie chicken and the sharp-tailed grouse, are now extensively sympatric, although this was not the case prior to homesteading. Hybrids between these species are very frequent in some

135

areas of recently acquired overlap (northern Michigan and on Manitoulin Island, Ontario), but are much rarer in the midwestern states, where there has been prolonged contact between them. A few other interspecific grouse hybrids have also occurred, but in general there are sufficiently great ecological requirement differences among the North American grouse to prevent much contact during reproductive periods. Where such contacts occur major differences in male displays and display structures presumably provide for reproductive isolation.

In spite of their tendency toward polygamy or promiscuity, grouse do not exhibit the extremes of plumage dimorphism described earlier for birds of paradise. Rather, the male signaling devices are usually well concealed except during actual display, when they are brought into sudden prominence (Fig. 6). Thus, male grouse typically possess a bare area of skin over the eyes that is variably engorged with blood, producing a brilliant "comb" that varies in color from red to yellow. In several species unfeathered neck areas called "air sacs" can be expanded by esophageal inflation; these differ in color, location, rate or amount of expansion, and associated sounds. The tail and undertail coverts are displayed in all species by tail-cocking, but the tail profiles, colors, and covert patterns differ. Additionally, the tail may be simply cocked, shaken, spread open and snapped shut, or widely fanned and sometimes tilted toward the female. Likewise, the folded wings may be symmetrically drooped and scrape the ground, rustled against specialized breast feathers, spread widely, or drooped asymmetrically on the side toward the female. Some species indulge in a conspicuous short flight called a "flutter jump" or a "drumming flight," but the male ruffed grouse remains on the ground throughout its drumming performance.

If enough information were available, it would be interesting to make comparisons with similarly dimorphic and polygamous groups such as the birds of paradise, hummingbirds, and manakins. Comparable degrees of sexual dimorphism in behavior and structure can be observed in various polygamous mammals such as the pinnipeds and many ungulates, but in these it is probable that sexual selection rather than selection for reproductive isolation has played a larger role in the evolution of these differences. Sexual dimorphism in the monkeys and apes varies considerably in the different groups, and in these primates both sources of selection may be significant. Such visual signals as manes, beards, mustaches, and colorful facial skin occur in males of numerous species, and marked sexual dimorphism in laryngeal struc-

Fig. 6. Male Displays of Greater Prairie Chicken (A), Sharp-tailed Grouse (B), Sage Grouse (C), Blue Grouse (D), Ruffed Grouse (E) and Spruce Grouse (F). Lines indicate reported hybrid combinations.

tures or associated air sacs is also present in some. Visual signals related to sexual recognition and reproductive cycles commonly occur in the genital regions of primates, and may functionally replace the olfactory signaling devices of more typical mammals. The social behavior and communication methods of the higher primates will now be considered in an attempt to consolidate the views presented in the earlier chapters and to examine how they might be applied to man.

SUGGESTED READING

BLAIR, W. F., "Isolating Mechanisms and Interspecies Interactions in Anuran Amphibians." *Quarterly Review of Biology* 39:334-344, 1964.

EHRMAN, L., "Courtship and Mating Behavior as a Reproductive Isolating Mechanism in *Drosophila.*" *American Zoologist* 4:147-153, 1964.

HUNSAKER, DON, "Ethological Isolating Mechanisms in the *Sceloporus torquatus* group of Lizards." *Evolution* 16:62-74, 1962.

JOHNSGARD, P. A., and WOOD, R., "Distributional Changes and Interaction between Prairie Chickens and Sharp-tailed Grouse in the Midwest." *Wilson Bulletin,* in press. (See also *Natural History* 66:16-21, March, 1967.)

MAYR, ERNST, *Animal Species and Evolution.* Cambridge, Mass.: Harvard University Press, 1963, 797 pp.

PERDECK, A. C., "The Isolating Value of Specific Song Patterns in Two Sibling Species of Grasshoppers (*Chortippus brunneus* Thunb. and *C. biguttulus* L.)." *Behaviour* 12:1-75, 1958.

SIBLEY, C. G., "Hybridization and Isolating Mechanisms." In *Vertebrate Speciation.* Austin: University of Texas Press, 1961, pp. 69-88.

SMITH, N. G., "Evolution of Some Arctic Gulls (*Larus*): An Experimental Study of Isolating Mechanisms." Monograph No. 4, American Ornithologists' Union, 1965, 99 pp.

SPIETH, H. T., "Behavior and Isolating Mechanisms." In ROE, A. and SIMPSON, G. G. (eds.), *Behavior and Evolution.* New Haven, Conn.: Yale University Press, 1958, pp. 363-389.

STORER, R. W., "Courtship and Mating Behavior and the Phylogeny of the Grebes." *Proceedings XIII International Ornithological Congress, Ithaca,* 1963, pp. 562-569.

CHAPTER 13

Behavior of higher primates

In the preceding chapters an attempt has been made to show that the behavior of any animal is an adaptive result of natural selection as innate and acquired responses are developed to cope with the physical habitat, the influence of other species, and intraspecific competition for space, food, and mates. Thus, depending on a species' capacity for genetic modification of its intrinsic attributes, adaptive behavioral responses are subject to evolutionary improvement. The question may now be raised: Can the behavior of man be explained in this same fashion, and can the impressive behavioral differences between modern man and the nonhuman primates be completely accounted for by evolutionary principles?

In an attempt to answer this question it is necessary to review some of the behavioral characteristics of the other primates, particularly those anatomically nearest to man. These latter are the anthropoid apes of the family Pongidae, which includes several species of gibbons (*Hylobates*), the orang utan (*Pongo*), the chimpanzee (*Pan*), and the gorilla (*Gorilla*). Some authorities would divide the gibbons into two genera, and others now believe that the gorilla and chimpanzee should be placed in the same genus, but there is general agreement that the gibbons are least similar anatomically to man and that the gorilla and chimpanzee, especially the latter, are closest to man. Of course, no modern zoologist believes that modern man (*Homo sapiens*) descended from gorillas or chimpanzees, but only that a common ancestral species existed from which the now-living forms were derived. The best recent evidence suggests that this splitting of gene pools occurred in the Old World between 10 and 25 million years ago. The African fossil *Proconsul* appears to be close to an ancestral chimpanzee-gorilla type, and the Indian fossil *Ramapithecus* of about the same age is somewhat closer to the supposed ancestral protohuman, although both are very apelike. Since we know nothing about the behavior of these fossil forms, it is necessary to use information from the living "great apes" and infer from this the probable behavior of the protohominid ancestors of man.

BEHAVIOR OF THE ANTHROPOID APES

Until a few years ago, little detailed information was available concerning the behavior of the manlike apes under natural conditions. All of the forms have been regularly exhibited in zoos, but clearly this source of information provides a rudimentary and often highly distorted picture of the normal behavioral adaptations of the species. The accounts of hunters, who usually shot first and later embellished their exploits, only increased the discrepancy between presumptions and facts. But in recent years zoologists in steadily increasing numbers have taken to the field and, in ethological fashion, have attempted to observe the great apes in their natural surroundings and to record their behavioral adjustments to situations they normally encounter. Their findings have forced a major revision in our attitudes on nearly every aspect of anthropoid behavior, and particularly on general aggressiveness, carnivorous tendencies, and capacities for tool use and construction. The outstanding reports of such persons as George Schaller on the orang utan and mountain gorilla, Jane Goodall on the chimpanzee, and C. R. Carpenter on the lar gibbon cannot be adequately summarized here. However, an attempt will be made to use some of their findings for comparative purposes, in hopes that a behavioral picture of the higher primates most akin to man will emerge. Emphasis will be placed on the chimpanzee and gorilla, since these two forms are clearly the most manlike, and since relatively less information is available concerning the orang utan and the gibbons.

Ecologically, all of the great apes are forest-dwellers, and to varying degrees all are arboreal. Orang utans and gibbons are almost strictly arboreal, but the chimpanzee is less so, and the gorilla is more nearly terrestrial. Home ranges of the gibbons appear to be relatively small (30 to 100 acres), but this situation may simply reflect the small average size of the groups (two to six animals). Home ranges of chimpanzees are much larger, and a typical group numbering some sixty to eighty animals may range from six to thirty square miles. Gorilla groups are evidently more cohesive in constitution and usually number less than two dozen animals which may range over an area of ten to fifteen square miles. All the great apes forage primarily on green vegetation, tubers, and fruits, occasionally supplemented in at least some species by meat. Predatory behavior by apes, usually directed toward young mammals, has been most frequently observed in chimpanzees. Chimpanzees are also known to fashion simple tools from branches, which they often use to extricate termites from their nests.

The social system of the great apes is probably basically a patriarchal system, with one or more adult males being dominant. This patriarchy appears to be especially prevalent in chimpanzees and gorillas. In chimpanzees there are usually several adult males in each social group which evidently lack distinct dominance relationships, whereas a linear dominance arrangement appears to be present in the males of mountain gorilla groups. Females of both species apparently lack definite dominance hierarchies. In nearly all the great apes promiscuity or polygyny occurs; wild gibbons, however, may be basically monogamous.

Apart from the gibbons, which primarily utilize bimanual locomotion (brachiation) and a small amount of bipedal walking, the great apes are essentially quadripedal. Although Vernon Reynolds has observed that wild chimpanzees often walk, run, and gallop in quadripedal fashion, he noted that bipedal walking on the ground is limited to less than ten paces. Walking in trees while using the hands for support occurs up to a distance of fifteen feet. Chimpanzees are also capable of horizontal leaps up to six feet, and vertical leaps downward as far as thirty feet. Bimanual locomotion methods include brachiation and swinging. George Schaller determined that bipedal locomotion is quite rare in mountain gorillas, and only twice did he see them cover more than twenty feet in this manner.

All of the great apes possess a large number of vocalizations. Estimates of the total number used by each species varies according to the observer; Vernon Reynolds reports twelve for the chimpanzee whereas Jane Goodall has distinguished twenty-three. Dr. Schaller distinguished twenty-one fairly distinct vocalizations in the mountain gorilla, but several were heard only once or a few times. In any case, the vocabularies of the great apes would appear to be much more limited than those of even the most primitive human tribes. But like their visual signals, ape vocalizations tend to be graded rather than all-or-none, and thus presumably a great range of motivational differences can be communicated. Further, most ape communication involves a combination of visual and auditory components, as well as olfactory or tactile stimuli in some instances. This intergrading and "constellation" effect of multiple simultaneous signals no doubt accounts for the difficulties of neatly totaling the numbers of different visual or vocal signals in the primates. Nonvocal acoustical signals, such as those produced by drumming on trees, slapping the ground, and beating the chest, occur in all the great apes with the possible exception of the gibbons. Perhaps the "wailing songs" of the gibbons replace such nonvocal communication in that group. These nonvocal sounds appear to be more uniform, or stereotyped, than primate vocalizations, and may be especially important for long-distance communication in the great apes. Various drumming methods are used by aboriginal humans for exactly the same function.

In their maintenance activities of eating, sleeping, and the like, the great apes show similarities to one another and to man. Drinking by chimpanzees may be done by sucking water off the arm or fingers, directly sucking water from a stream, or dipping a crumpled leaf into water and then sucking the liquid from it. Sleeping may occur in a sitting posture in the crotch of a tree (gibbons), or on a nest of vegetation built in trees or (gorillas) on the ground. In chimpanzees and gorillas a new nest is constructed each day or, if an old site is used, new branches are added to it. When sleeping, the animals may lie sideways, on their backs, or in other postures similar to those assumed by sleeping humans.

Mutual grooming appears to be a widespread social pattern in the primates and occurs in all the great apes. Besides its obvious hygienic function, grooming probably serves as a very important tactile stimulus. Mutual grooming is evidently most significant as a social integration mechanism in those species lacking well-developed dominance hierarchies. Thus, mutual grooming is not common in free-living gorillas, but is quite prevalent in chimpanzees. In that species grooming occurs within and between age classes, and within and between sexes. Males particularly tend to groom estrus females, and such females may be groomed by more than one male consecutively.

EVOLUTION OF HUMAN BEHAVIOR

We may next compare the behavior of humans with that of the great apes to observe the similarities and try to account for the differences.

A large number of similarities are clearly present. Both humans and the other higher primates have ill-defined or totally absent breeding seasons, and instead bear young at any time of the year. This unusual situation is largely a reflection of the regular monthly female menstrual cycles, but a definite estrus cycle is present only in nonhumans. Normally only a single young is born, and it is provided with prolonged maternal care lasting several years. The female's total attention to the dependent young is associated with a patriarchal social system in which the larger males assume responsibility for protecting the family.

Certain sensory and motor abilities are also typical of both humans and the simian primates. These include binocular color vision correlated with frontally located eyes and diurnal activity patterns, and a reduced sense of smell associated with a shorter muzzle extension and smaller nasal area than occur in other mammals. A final similarity between man and nearly all other primates is the presence of an opposable thumb. This climbing adaptation (which also occurs in various climbing marsupials) provides for a "power grip," and is of particular importance for maintaining tree-climbing abilities among the relatively large-bodied monkeys and apes. But the increasing utilization by apes of the thumb for manipulative purposes, and the development of a tool-using "precision grip" that supplemented the power grip as the thumb became more dextrous, provides a significant key to the evolution of human behavior.

In several respects humans represent the termination of a general evolutionary trend in anatomy and behavior, the beginnings of which can often be detected in the Old World monkeys. For example, humans exhibit the longest time to sexual maturity (about twelve to fourteen years, vs. six to ten for the anthropoids and two to four for the Old World monkeys), and the longest period of infant dependency on the mother (six to eight years in humans, vs. about two or three in anthropoids, and one year in monkeys). Humans also exhibit by far the largest actual and relative brain size in the primates, and the anthropoids show a distinct advancement toward this condition beyond that found in the Old World monkeys. The differences in this regard between man and the anthropoids are marked. Thus, it seems probable that the situation in man is not so much the termination of a general series as the direct result of natural selection favoring increases in brain size and cortical complexity.

This last anatomical hiatus between man and apes brings us to the third category of comparison; those traits by which man differs markedly from the anthropoids. Most of these are related to the fact that man is a strictly bipedal species, whereas the anthropoids utilize this means of locomotion only secondarily. Undoubtedly the assumption of a permanently upright stance (which probably occurred at least two million years ago, judging from the fossil evidence of African ape men) was preeminent in shaping the behavioral evolution of men. By standing erect, and adopting a terrestrial rather than arboreal habitat, the hands of the earliest hominids were freed to wield tools and weapons, and the significance of powerful jaws, long canines, and brute strength withered before the supremacy of intelligence and weapons. Thus, the development of efficient tool or weapon construction and use was dependent upon improved mental abilities, and no doubt this development was the primary source of natural selection favoring increased brain size and complexity.

The gradually enlarging brain and permanently erect stance brought both advantages and disadvantages. The advantages included conversion from a basically herbivorous diet to a largely carnivorous one, as increasingly larger animals fell prey to early man's hunting techniques. Probably, hunting larger animals demanded greater cooperation between individuals, requiring the aggregation of larger cooperative social groups, greater home ranges, more efficient communication systems, and perhaps precipitating the first forms of territorial warfare. The increasing interdependence of males in their hunting efforts made the accumulation of large harems impractical and probably limited the number of females that a single male could readily provide for. A kind of economic monogamy thus became superimposed on what had probably been a basically polygamous system, and radically changed the social organization of early human society. Individual male and female relationships gradually became more permanent, a situation fostered by the modification of the estrus cycle into a condition of more or less continuous female receptivity. This increasing stability of families probably facilitated the development of permanent family-sized shelters for rest and protection, in contrast to the temporary nests and communal refuges of the anthropoids.

As the human body gradually adapted to an erect posture the pelvic bones were reshaped and the size of the public canal was relatively reduced. At the same time the skull was becoming larger as the brain increased in size. These changes demanded that the young be born at a less advanced stage, before the head became too large for the birth canal. At birth the average human's brain is less than one fourth full size, whereas a newborn ape's brain is slightly over half its adult size, a proportion that is not reached in the human baby until about the end of its first year. Undoubtedly this "premature birth" accounts for the slower motor development of human children as compared with young apes. The shifted body stance also affected the position of the female's external genitalia, making physical restraint and sexual assault by males more likely than is the case in quadripedal animals.

As vocalizations became more elaborate, communication systems developed extensive *vocabularies* that included words indicating both concrete objects and abstract ideas. Unlike animal signals having only immediate significance, human languages contain words which may objectively describe past or present events, and which may subjectively contemplate the past, present, or future. Thus, various *traditions* that were transmitted orally between generations gradually developed, and *cultural evolution* soon became more significant than biological evolution in the shaping of human behavior patterns. The universal human tendency to manipulate and shape objects probably produced sculptured figures or drawings in the form of animals or humans. The utilization of such totems and icons as talismans to allay superstitious fears, or in hunting or fertility rites, may have provided the basis for primitive forms of worship. In this manner traditional ceremonies slowly grew into formal cults and sects, and paved the way for the establishment of complex religions. Such unifying religious activities probably provided a stabilizing influence on the emerging societies, which might otherwise have been constantly in danger of internecine warfare. Furthermore, religious taboos on incest, promiscuity, and other aspects of sexual behavior may have been necessary to cope with the changing social relationships outlined above. Thus did modern human society have its earliest beginnings.

Three aspects of human behavioral evolution deserve special attention — the evolution of weapon use and carnivorous behavior, the evolution of human languages from primate vocalizations, and the evolution of human expressions and other visual signals. Most of the elements of protohominid weapon use and incipient predatory behavior can be observed in the various living primates. For example, in the agonistic behavior of the larger great apes such responses as throwing objects and clubbing behavior have been observed, according to Adriaan Kortlandt and M. Kooij. Incipient predatory behavior consisting of catching, killing, and eating freshly killed game has also been occasionally reported in various great apes or Old World monkeys. It has therefore been suggested that the use of tools as weapons preceded their use as "gadgets," and that there was an early development of human pleasure in killing and torture that unfortunately appears to have been retained to the present time.

The evolution of primate vocalizations can be traced even further backward than that of tool use, as shown by the work of Richard Andrew. He has suggested that the calls of nonhuman primates can be grouped into a number of functional categories, at least some of which can be related to human vocalizations. Warning calls in the primates probably evolved as a result of the importance of vision and the close and prolonged parental relationship in primates. Like the warning calls of passerine birds, two types of primate warning signals exist. One functions as a mobbing call, such as the barking of chimpanzees, but the others is more difficult to locate and is used for more dangerous predators. Contact calls may have first developed between mothers and their young, or between the sexes during periods of breeding, and later may have been elaborated to include other members of the social group. Quite probably the conversational communication between humans developed from such contact calls. Two other types of primate calls include greeting calls, perhaps derived from those sounds given by infants when searching for their mother's breast, and the wailing songs of lemurs and gibbons, which may be used for long-distance communication.

Among man's simpler nonconversational vocalizations there are many similarities to those of chimpanzees. For example, both utter segmented grunting sounds during laughing, and infants of both use laughing as a greeting. Likewise, crying sounds are similar. Other "primitive" utterances of humans include the grunting noises made by an individual confronted with an interesting object, and the "Ooh" of surprise, which may correspond to the warning note of chimpanzees.

The evolution of facial expressions in the higher primates has also been the subject of recent study by several people, including J. Van Hoof. He has pointed out that the evolution of facial expressions was dependent upon a variety of factors, and as a result such expressions are largely limited to primates, carnivores, and ungulates, which are largely diurnal, have good eyesight, and probably utilize their expressions as signals.

Van Hoof concluded that facial expressions of the higher primates are the compound result of different motivational tendencies, and are largely the reflection of agonistic conflicts or conflicts between social attraction and fleeing. Primarily agonistic expressions can be grouped into a hierarchy of four general categories that were present in all the species he studied. They include the expressions of "attack," "aggressive threat," "scared threat," and, in trapped defensive situations, the "crouch." These differ especially in the degree to which the mouth is opened and the teeth are exposed. Four expressions appear to result from conflict between social attraction and fleeing. "Grinning," an expression involving exposure of teeth, may be an appeasement gesture or is possibly a protective startle response to a sudden change in stimulation. "Lip-smacking" and "teeth-chattering" are social expressions often elicited during greeting or grooming between individuals. The last of the four expressions in this category is the "flehmen" expression, which appears to result from smelling with protruded lips, and may be performed by males during sexual excitement. Two final expressions observed are the "pout," which is also performed with somewhat protruded lips and appears to be a means of requesting cooperation such as during begging for food or comfort, and "play," which occurs during playful activity. This last expression can be induced in chimpanzees by tickling, and in both chimpanzees and gorillas a laughing noise may accompany it.

Charles Darwin was the first biologist to compare critically the expressions of humans and nonhuman primates; his book on animal expressions may thus be regarded as the first of all ethological monographs. At the time very little information was available on expressions of nonhuman primates, and Darwin had to resort to comparisons between races or societies of humans, between infants and adults, and between totally blind or insane and normal individuals to prove the universality of certain human expressions. He thus proved that the facial expressions associated with grief are of universal human occurrence and can be largely accounted for by an anatomical analysis of the muscle movements involved with the physiological changes associated with this mental state. Such pleasurable expressions as smiling, laughing, and gestures of affection that involve touching other individuals are likewise species-typical and have exact parallels among the anthropoid apes. The basically agonistic expressions that range from utter rage (the "frenzy" of chimpanzees) through anger, astonishment, and finally terror may also be directly related to the similar spectrum of agonistic expressions in other primates. Thus, Darwin observed that the human

147

expression of sneering involves the exposure of the canine tooth on one side, and may be comparable to the snarling of other mammals. He regarded blushing as the most peculiarly human of all emotions, and emphasized that it is the result of mental rather than physical stimulation. But blushing is clearly produced by stimulation of the sympathetic nervous system, and as such is probably homologous to the flushing of the facial skin observed in other species in times of mental or physical stress.

George Schaller has also provided some observations that suggest the importance of facial expressions, sounds, and physical gestures as social signals in gorillas. He reports a range of visual threat gestures that include an unwavering stare or turning toward the opponent, an incipient charge, an incomplete charge, and finally an actual attack with biting and wrestling. Submissive gestures include turning the head to one side and avoiding the opponent's stare, shaking the head, and cowering by lowering the head and tucking the hands and legs under the abdomen. The similarities between these signals and the corresponding agonistic responses of humans are almost too obvious to mention.

The gorilla's aggressive signals have to a large degree been ritualized into various displays, of which the "chest-beating" sequence is most famous. This display is actually a complex combination of visual and auditory signals, which may be incompletely and variably performed. In its full version the sequence includes about nine distinct components. The sequence often starts with "hooting," a series of loud sounds increasing in tempo and similar to those uttered by gibbons. Next, "symbolic feeding," such as plucking a leaf and putting it between the teeth, sometimes occurs. The animal might then stand bipedally ("rising") and toss vegetation into the air ("throwing"). "Chest-beating," a rapid, alternate slapping of the chest, is the most stereotyped part of the sequence. "Leg-kicking" may occur during chest-beating, and sideways "running" may terminate the beating sequence. During or after this running the gorilla may perform "slapping and tearing" of the vegetation, and usually terminates the entire sequence with "ground-thumping," consisting of a slapping of the ground with the palm of the hand. Such a conspicuous display is no doubt highly effective in warning others without resorting to more overt aggression, but it also occurs during other times of emotional stress or may even be performed in rudimentary fashion without obvious stimulation. The close similarities between these gestures, calls, and movements, and those performed by "cheerleaders" and spectators at such exciting and tension-filled sports as football are too strikingly similar to resist comparison. Although these human responses are clearly under voluntary control, one cannot help wondering whether they are not really a reflection of fundamental primate behavior patterns released under the stimulation of intense emotion.

Some human responses occurring in conflict situations probably represent displacement activities, such as yawning or handling one's hair or beard (both of which also occur in monkeys), or even falling asleep at a time when alertness is mandatory (during examinations or prior to going into battle). Men often perform senseless redirected aggression toward subordinate individuals (wives, children, pets) or inanimate objects (kicking a table, pounding the walls, *etc.*). Finally, with all his impressive mental abilities, the human species is just as vulnerable to artificial supernormal stimulations as is the gull vainly trying to incubate a giant wooden egg, or a tropic-bird (*Phaëthon*) attempting to mate with a model glider. Indeed, the whole fashion and cosmetics industry depends on this astonishing sensitivity of humans to artificial visual signals and enhanced olfactory stimulation by the opposite sex.

Recalling Charles Darwin's great interest in and respect for animals, and his knowledge of the all too frequent fallibility and cruelty of the human species, it is easy to sympathize with his view that he would rather have descended from apelike ancestors than "from a savage who delights to torture his enemies, offers up bloody sacrifices, practices infanticide without remorse, treats his wives like slaves, knows no decency, and is haunted by the grossest superstitions." It is hoped that this review of animal behavior patterns will allow the reader better to evaluate and interpret what he might observe in watching the "lower" animals, and also perhaps better to understand the many equally remarkable facets of human behavior.

SUGGESTED READING

ANDREW, R. J., "The Origin and Evolution of the Calls and Facial Expressions of the Primates." *Bahaviour* 20:1-109, 1963.
———, "The Origins of Facial Expressions." *Scientific American*, October, 1965, pp. 88-94. (Available in offprint form.)
CARPENTER, C. R., *Naturalistic Behavior of Nonhuman Primates*. University Park: Pennsylvania State University Press, 1964, 454 pp.

149

DARWIN, C., *The Expressions of the Emotions in Man and Animals.* New York: D. Appleton and Company, 1873, 374 pp. (Available in softback form from the University of Chicago Press, Chicago.)

DEVORE, IRVEN (ed.), *Primate Behavior.* New York: Holt, Rinehart and Winston, Inc., 1965, 654 pp.

EIMERL, S., and DEVORE, I., *The Primates* ("Life Nature Library"). New York: Time Inc. Book Division, 1965, 200 pp.

GOODALL, JANE, "My Life Among Wild Chimpanzees." *National Geographic Magazine,* August, 1963, pp. 273-308.

KORTLANDT, A., "Chimpanzees in the Wild." *Scientific American,* May, 1962, pp. 128-138. (Available in offprint form.)

NAPIER, JOHN, "The Evolution of the Hand." *Scientific American,* June, 1962, pp. 56-62. (Available in offprint form.)

SCHALLER, G. B., *The Mountain Gorilla: Ecology and Behavior.* Chicago: University of Chicago Press, 1963, 462 pp. (Also, softback *Year of the Gorilla,* Ballantine Books, New York.)

SOUTHWICK, C. H., *Primate Social Behavior.* Princeton, N. J.: D. Van Nostrand Company, Inc., 1963, 191 pp.

WASHBURN, S. L., and AVIS, VIRGINIA, "Evolution of Human Behavior." In ROE, A. and SIMPSON, G. G. (eds.), *Behavior and Evolution,* New Haven, Conn.: Yale University Press, 1958, 557 pp.

Index

151

Dabbling ducks (Anatinae), 90, 126
eiders (*Somateria* and *Polysticta*), 116, 126
mallard (*Anas*), 40, 90, 114
pintail (*Anas*), 49, 90

Watson, J. B., 2
Wecker, S. C., 92
Whitman, C., 2, 106
Whitten effect, 80
Wood-Gush, D., 89